Getting Agriculture Moving

This book has been written as part of a project of the Agricultural Development Council, Inc. to select and prepare teaching materials for use in Asia, Africa and Latin America. The project is financed by a grant from the Ford Foundation.

A training manual, and a set of selected readings related to the chapter topics of this book are available from the Agricultural Development Council, Inc., 630 Fifth Avenue, New York, N. Y. 10020

Since this book is primarily a review of facts and ideas that are already common knowledge, it does not include footnotes giving references to sources. It is a synthesis of such materials rather than a report of original research. Only the organization of the materials, and a few of the implications for agricultural development drawn from widely known facts and ideas, are original contributions of the author.

Photographs courtesy of:
Food and Agriculture Organization of the United Nations
United Nations
Association for Credit and Rural Assistance—Brazil
Belgian Information Institute
Rockefeller Foundation
Del Monte Corporation
F. Shuman
United States Department of Agriculture
Allahabad Agricultural Institute

GETTING AGRICULTURE MOVING

Essentials for Development and Modernization

Arthur T. Mosher

Published for
The Agricultural Development Council

by
Frederick A. Praeger, *Publishers*
New York • Washington • London

HD1415
·M55

FREDERICK A. PRAEGER, *Publishers*
111 Fourth Avenue, New York, N. Y. 10003, U.S.A.
77-79 Charlotte Street, London, W.1, England

Published in the United States of America in 1966
by Frederick A. Praeger, Inc., Publishers, for the
Agricultural Development Council, Inc.,
630 Fifth Avenue, New York

Library of Congress Catalog Card Number: 66-17367
Printed in the United States of America by Sowers Printing Company,
Lebanon, Pennsylvania

Book and cover design by John E. Jamison
Illustrations by Edd Ashe

Preface

This book is about making agriculture more productive—more productive to the country in which it is located while providing a better living for the farm people who engage in it. More particularly, the book is about needs and problems at early stages of agricultural development. Hence the title: *Getting Agriculture Moving.*

The deeper one goes into a study of agricultural development, the more convinced one becomes that development depends on the understanding of agricultural development itself, as well as on the specialized skills of a wide variety of persons engaged in many occupations and activities in each country attempting to develop its agriculture. Such understanding is needed not only by planners and administrators but by legislators and editors, extension and research workers, merchants, bankers, educators, and many others. This understanding can be promoted by regular courses of study in schools and colleges. It can be stimulated by editorials, news stories and feature articles in newspapers and magazines, and by radio, newsreels and even television programs. At early stages of agricultural development, regular and repeated in-service training programs for personnel of all agencies related to agriculture can be particularly effective in advancing understanding of agricultural development.

The principal purpose of this book is to serve as a framework for systematic discussion of the development process in agriculture in in-service training programs. Such discussion must draw on many materials other than this book. To aid in assembling such materials, the Agricultural Development Council has collected, and is arranging to make available, a variety of readings, illustrations and case

5

materials related to the topic of each chapter, and a training manual containing suggestions for the use of these.

Ideally, illustrations and cases used in each training course on agricultural development should include many from the country in which the course is being given. For the most part, these will have to be added locally. All that this book, and the other materials being made available by the Council, can do is to provide a framework for the discussion, and a body of generalizations based on comparing experiences in many countries. Each of these generalizations, rather than being accepted at face value, needs to be made a topic for critical discussion in the light of local circumstances and experiences.

While the primary purpose of this book is to serve as a basis for discussion in programs of in-service training, it is hoped that persons of influence in each country into whose hands the book comes will take the time to read it carefully. Agricultural development is a complex topic. Too frequently, we fall into the error of seizing on one or another single activity or type of program as being a panacea for all of the ills of agriculture. At the other extreme, a catalog of *all* of the factors affecting agricultural productivity can lead to such diffusion of effort that little is accomplished. What we have tried to do in this book is to identify the major factors that affect agricultural development and to distinguish between those that are *essential* and those that can *accelerate* development in those places where the essentials have been met.

Many people played important parts in the preparation of this book. All members of the staff of the Agricultural Development Council and a number of correspondents in many countries have provided materials and criticized early drafts. A preliminary draft was discussed with consultants in seminars in the Philippines and in East and West Africa.

In a sense this book is still a preliminary draft. Agricultural development is a subject on which we all have much to learn. The author will welcome criticisms of the book and suggestions for its improvement.

A. T. MOSHER

New York
October 1965

6

CONTENTS

		Page
Preface		5
Introduction		9

PART I The Elements of Agriculture

Chapter	1. The Production Process	15
	2. The Farmer	25
	3. The Farm	39
	4. The Farm Business	51

PART II The Essentials for Agricultural Development

Chapter	5. Markets for Farm Products	63
	6. Constantly Changing Technology	75
	7. Local Availability of Supplies and Equipment	89
	8. Production Incentives for Farmers	99
	9. Transportation	111

PART III The Accelerators of Agricultural Development

Chapter	10. Education for Development	123
	11. Production Credit	141
	12. Group Action by Farmers	153
	13. Improving and Expanding Agricultural Land	162
	14. National Planning for Agricultural Development	169

PART IV

	15. Getting Agriculture Moving	182

Introduction

To increase the agricultural production of a country is a complex task. It is frequently a baffling task as well. It is complex because so many different conditions have to be created or modified, by different persons and groups of people. It is baffling because the *spirit* of a people is involved also. Techniques are not enough. They have to be combined and used with intelligence, imagination, experimentation, and continuing hard work. Agricultural development is as dependent on how effectively people work together as it is on the natural resources with which they begin.

Yet agricultural development does occur. Farmers experiment with new crops, frequently with no other encouragement than seeing these grow in neighbors' fields. Research workers develop new strains of crops and discover improved practices in the use of fertilizers and in the management of soil moisture. Engineers, and sometimes individual farmers, produce improved implements. Merchants develop better methods of handling farm products brought to the market and better and cheaper ways of transporting them. Governments adopt new patterns of land holding, taxation policies and price policies that make the adoption of better farming methods more profitable. These and many other steps to increase agricultural production have their effect.

Our task in this book is to examine the great variety of factors affecting agricultural development, noting what each accomplishes and how each depends for its effect on each of the others.

We are frequently misled by the greater success of a few farmers into thinking the task of development is easier than it is. Examples that stand out like islands of progressive farming in an ocean of primitive cultivation usually are due to a combination of especially favorable circumstances and to a farmer of exceptional skill. It is foolish to think that thousands of other farmers lack only the *will* to get similar results on their own farms. That certainly is needed. But it will never be possible for every farmer to be located on the best land, with the greatest access to markets and farm supplies and equipment. Nor is it possible for every farmer to have the highest skill. There always will be differences in farming ability as well as in agricultural resources. One of the main tasks in agricultural development is to find ways of farming that farmers of typical ability can use effectively if only they will learn a little more and develop somewhat better skills. Another is to find more productive uses for farms of only moderate productivity, along with practicable means of increasing the land's fertility. Other tasks are to create resources of education, farm supplies, credit and market outlets that make it not too difficult for all farmers who are willing to work at it to raise the productivity of their farms.

Another way in which it is easy to err is to think that agriculture is essentially primitive and that the really "modern" types of production are all to be found in urban industries. This is not true. While much of agriculture is primitive it need not be. Whether it is primitive or progressive depends partly on the knowledge, skill and diligence of farmers and partly on the facilities with which the whole nation surrounds each farmer. Of course, the same could be said of urban industries. They are by no means all modern and progressive either.

Agricultural development is needed in almost every country of the world today. The race between increasing population and mankind's food supply is real and grim. Agriculture is the only way we now know to produce the food on which our very lives depend. To feed the additional millions of people being added to the world's population each year, and to improve somewhat the present inadequate amount of food per person, will require faster agricultural development in the next two decades than almost any country has ever achieved in the past.

The farmers of the world, and their families, need agricultural development in order that they may live better. It is only by producing more, and selling more, that they can buy some of the many things they need and want for a more satisfactory level of living.

The total number of these farmers will not soon decrease no matter how hard each country tries to industrialize. Establishing new industries costs so much in machinery and equipment for each job it makes available, and population is growing so rapidly, that the most that can be hoped for is to provide non-farm employment for the annual *increase* in the number of people needing employment. Some countries will find it difficult to do even this. Reducing the number of farmers in a country's population comes relatively late in the process of development. Even in Japan, noted for its industrial development, there was no reduction in the number of persons dependent on farming for their livelihood from 1870 to 1940, and the number only dropped from 14,500,000 to 14,200,000 between 1940 and 1960. During the same period, from 1870 to 1960, non-agricultural employment rose from 3,000,000 to 18,000,000.

Each nation that has a substantial number of farmers needs agricultural development for additional reasons. In order to industrialize —and nearly every nation needs to industrialize—it needs increased earnings from agriculture to pay part of the costs of industrialization. Industrial equipment must usually be purchased abroad, and increased agricultural exports can be an important way to earn the foreign exchange needed to pay for it. And industries must have markets for their products. The larger the market for these within the country itself, the faster can industries grow. If the incomes of farmers remain so low that they can make few purchases, domestic industries will be retarded in their development.

Agricultural and Human Development

We are likely to think and talk of agricultural development as being valuable only because it makes more farm products available for human use. In fact, it has an additional, and perhaps a more important product: it changes the people who engage in it.

For agricultural development to occur, the knowledge and skill of farmers must keep increasing and changing. As farmers adopt more and more new methods, their ideas change. They develop a new and different attitude toward agriculture, toward the natural world that

11

surrounds them, and toward themselves. Their early successes in increasing production increase their self-confidence. Their increasing contacts and transactions with merchants and government agencies draw them into closer acquaintance with the world beyond their villages. They increasingly become *citizens,* full members of the nation.

A similar transformation occurs among research workers, extension agents, government officials, merchants, bankers, teachers and many others. The same changes that result in added agricultural production bring about changes in the persons who participate in them.

Agricultural development thus is an integral part of general social and economic development. It contributes to it, and it assures that the over-all development shall be truly general, including within its scope the large proportion of people who live by farming—and who will for many years continue to live by farming in many countries.

Agricultural development is a social product. It is not the result of the work of farmers alone. It is a result of the activities of farmers and farm families, lawmakers, highway engineers, merchants, manufacturers, research workers, teachers, veterinarians, editors, and every citizen who participates in electing public officials and influencing the laws of his country.

PART

I

The Elements
of Agriculture

The first step toward getting agriculture moving is to achieve a clear and full understanding of what agriculture is.

Agriculture is a special kind of production based on the growth processes of plants and animals. *Farmers* manage and stimulate plant and animal growth on *farms*. The production activities on each farm are a *business* in which costs and returns are important.

We begin, then, with a review of the elements of agriculture.

The Production Process (Chapter 1)
The Farmer (Chapter 2)
The Farm (Chapter 3)
The Farm Business (Chapter 4)

13

The Production Process

Plants are the primary factories of agriculture. They take in carbon dioxide from the air through their leaves. They take in moisture and chemical substances from the soil through their roots. Out of these, using the energy of sunlight, they make seeds, fruits, fibers and oils that man can use.

Livestock are important secondary factories of agriculture. Depending on plants for their food, they can eat many parts of plants that man does not, such as the stems and leaves of grasses. They transform plant materials into still other products of use to man: meat, hides, wool, eggs and milk.

The growth of plants and animals goes on in nature without any participation by man. Thousands of kinds of plants have evolved over time in different parts of the world in response to differences in sunlight, temperature, amount of available moisture, and the nature of the soil. Each kind of plant has its own special requirements. It grows best with a certain growing season, certain temperatures at different stages of its growth, a certain amount of moisture, and certain soil characteristics.

The plants that grow in a particular region determine what kinds of animals, birds and insects live there, since some of these feed on the particular kinds of plants found in the region, while others feed on each other. As a result, different combinations of plants and animals are found in different parts of the world. Sometimes, particularly where the land is hilly or mountainous, these combinations are different within very short distances because of pronounced differences in temperature, direct sunlight, moisture and soil conditions.

Agriculture arises when man begins to *take control* of this growth of plants and animals, rearranging it to his own benefit. The difference between primitive and scientific agricultures lies in the degree to which this control has advanced.

In the most primitive agriculture, man accepts the soil, the rainfall, and the local strains of crop plants. He fosters the growth of these plants by eliminating to some degree the competition of other plants for the available sunlight and moisture. He tries, by primitive methods, to protect his crops from wild animals, birds, and insects. He domesticates certain animals, taking care of them and using their products.

In a scientific agriculture man applies his ingenuity to increasing his control over all the factors that affect plant and animal growth. He introduces irrigation and drainage. He adds plant nutrients to the soil. He breeds modified plants that are more resistant to disease, that can utilize large amounts of fertilizers, that are resistant to drought, that can mature more quickly, and that yield more of the particular products he wants. He develops scientifically prepared feeds for his

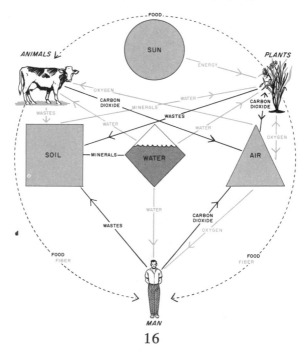

16

Farming can be primitive. Subsistence agriculture in Northern Togo

Or scientific. Irrigated rice in Japan

livestock and scientific methods to protect them from disease.

Certain characteristics of the biological production process of agriculture are beyond our control. We cannot change its dependence on the energy of sunshine or its variation with the seasons of the year. We cannot eliminate the great diversity of the many combinations of climate, topography, and soil that favor the growth of different types of plants and animals.

And yet, although man did not invent and does not fully understand the process of plant and animal growth, he has learned a great deal about them and has discovered many ways to control them for his own benefit. We are discovering new ways all the time through scientific research. This increasing knowledge provides the technical basis for the changes that add up to agricultural development.

Implications for Agricultural Development

Several important implications for agricultural development follow directly from the nature of the biological production processes of agriculture.

Agriculture must remain widely dispersed. Because the energy for plant growth comes from sunlight, agriculture cannot be concentrated in urban factories that can have their energy brought to them in the form of fuels or electrical energy. Agriculture will always require large areas of the earth's surface on which sunlight falls. This means, first of all, that a widespread transportation network is necessary for scientific agriculture, to take improved seeds, fertilizers, pesticides, and other modern production supplies and equipment to the various parts of the wide expanse of fields exposed to sunlight, and to bring agricultural products to markets.

Another consequence is that farmers cannot be moved out of their family and village setting into a more controlled "production environment." In non-agricultural industry, workers can be assembled in urban factories away from the places where they live. In agriculture, the changes necessary to increase productivity must be carried on in the midst of traditional family and village influences.

In contrast to the concentrated nature of cities and factory work, agriculture needs space to take advantage of soil and sunlight

18

Agriculture must vary markedly from place to place, frequently within short distances. We are not likely in the near future to be able to modify climates substantially, except in greenhouse agriculture. Even if we could, existing soils are the result of long evolution under various past climatic conditions. The differences in climates and soils call for different crops, adapted to differences in local environments.

In a few exceptional regions of the earth, conditions for plant growth are reasonably uniform over large areas of valuable agricultural land. The Nile Delta; the Corn Belt of the United States; the Ukraine Region of Russia; the rice regions of Thailand, Indonesia, the Philippines and Burma; the rubber regions of Malaysia, the coffee regions of Brazil, Colombia and East and West Africa, the grasslands of Australia, Uruguay, and the steppes of Asia—are examples of such regions. Within any one of these the uniformity is usually far from complete. Minor differences in soil and topography make different crops and soil treatments most productive.

Other regions are much more varied. Within short distances—frequently within a hundred steps—differences in soils and, in hilly country, differences in direct sunlight and temperatures call for different crops in order to make the best use of the local resources. Thus a small farm in Japan may combine rice with vegetables, bamboo and fish culture. A farm in North India may combine intensive irrigated cropping near a well with extensive dry-land farming only a hundred yards away. A farm in the Cauca Valley of Colombia may have one kind of crop on well-drained fields and another kind on a nearby field that is marshy.

These differences have important implications for agricultural development. Perhaps the most important is that they call for such close adaptation of crops and methods to varying local conditions that only the individual farmer can have the specialized knowledge of his farm necessary to make intelligent decisions about its use. This helps explain why so many programs that take much of the decision-making away from cultivators of individual farms and place it with national "plans" or with managers of large "collectives" fall far short of expectations. It is only where natural conditions are very uniform that large farms or plantations, with one manager directing the work of many "laborers" can match the efficiency of good individual farmer-operators of much smaller farms. Such uniformity of natural conditions is the exception rather than the rule.

Another important implication is that hints as to how the agriculture of a region can be improved can frequently be found by looking at the agriculture of other farms in the same region or at those in similar regions elsewhere in the world. But the importance of minor variations in soils and climates even in regions that seem similar means that crops or methods imported from other regions, or even from elsewhere in the same region, require careful testing to make sure they would prove satisfactory if adopted locally.

The timing of farming operations must be fitted to weather conditions and to attacks by pests and diseases. Factory production processes are carried on under controlled conditions that permit each operation to be performed at any time and all the time. Agricultural production, on the other hand, is subject to weather and to other factors such as the incidence of insect pests or diseases that vary from time to time and from place to place. Some operations, like plowing, can be done only when weather and soil conditions are right. Other operations, such as pest control, must be carried out quickly if a crop is threatened with destruction. Thus many agricultural operations cannot be rigidly scheduled in advance or from a distance. Schedules must be left flexible for on-the-spot decisions by each farmer, based on local conditions at the time.

The time factor in plant and animal growth favors diversification in agriculture. The basic biological production processes of agriculture have built-in time sequences and time requirements. Rice, maize, wheat, and other crop plants have their seasonal patterns of growth from sowing to harvest. Only at certain times in these growth cycles is human labor required. At other times there is nothing to do but wait.

Where there is a suitable combination of crops on the same farm, the workers need not be idle during these waiting periods. Growing different crops with different sowing-times and harvest-times spreads the use of labor over the year. When work is not needed on one crop, it can be devoted to another. Tending livestock also helps achieve a better distribution of labor, particularly where the livestock require the most attention during the time of the year when crops are

21

not in the field. Diversification can permit greater total production through more continuous use of labor.[1]

Most farm operators and laborers must have a wider variety of skills than factory workers. The time factor in plant and animal growth gives rise to a further difference between agriculture and other industries. Farmers and farm laborers need to be more versatile in their skills than workers in industrial plants where seasons play no part and all of the different stages of the production process can be carried on at the same time, each by a different set of workers. In most of agriculture, specialization of labor cannot go so far: each man must have a variety of skills. The need for versatility is particularly great where several crops and different livestock enterprises are combined on one farm.

Each change in a farming practice calls for additional changes. From the intimate adjustment of plants in their natural state to different local factors we may draw a further implication: that one change of a cultivation practice makes other changes advisable. The addition of fertilizer is usually necessary for any substantial increase in crop yields. But the full increase that might be brought about by fertilizer cannot be realized without introducing or breeding new strains of crops that can respond to it. The varieties that give the best yield without fertilizers are those that have developed in response to the present level of plant food nutrients in the soil. It takes a different strain of plant to make full use of additional fertilizer.

Similarly, in many areas substantial increase in yields requires more moisture than the rainfall or existing irrigation makes available. But the present varieties of crops have evolved in adjustment to limited moisture. When more moisture is made available it is usually necessary to introduce new varieties of crops that can respond to it.

With rice, for example, increasing water and fertilizer without changing the variety often results in lodging of the plants—they fall

---

[1] This reason for diversification does not apply in rice culture in a climate like that of parts of Java and Bali where rice can be sown at any time in the year. In such circumstances, planting different fields of a farm to the same crop but at different times can result in a good distribution of use of labor throughout the year.

There are, of course, other reasons for diversification, such as that different crops make different demands on soil moisture and nutrients, and some even contribute nutrients, so that rotation of crops permits higher yields.

Variety of Crops • INDIA

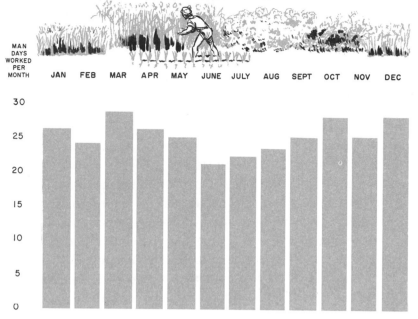

MAN DAYS WORKED PER MONTH

| JAN | FEB | MAR | APR | MAY | JUNE | JULY | AUG | SEPT | OCT | NOV | DEC |

30
25
20
15
10
5
0

Rice Only • PHILLIPINES

OPERATOR
HIRED TRANSPLANTER
HIRED HARVESTER

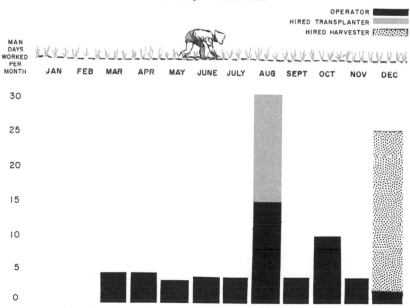

MAN DAYS WORKED PER MONTH

| JAN | FEB | MAR | APR | MAY | JUNE | JULY | AUG | SEPT | OCT | NOV | DEC |

30
25
20
15
10
5
0

"Growing different crops with different sowing-times and harvest-times spreads the use of labor over the year."

23

down before they mature. Part of the task of the plant breeder is then to breed a variety with a stiffer stem that will allow it to stand up under heavier applications of water and fertilizer.

A progressive agriculture is always changing. We often hear someone say, "We must substitute modern agriculture for our present primitive pattern of cultivation." Too often this attitude reflects the notion that there is "a" modern agriculture, and that once it has been adopted the task is done. This is not true. *A progressive agriculture is always changing.* Parts of it are always becoming obsolete. Each step forward makes other forward steps possible.

With scientific plant breeding the possibilities of crop improvement are enormous. Each new variety permits improvements in cultural practices; these in turn open additional opportunities for varietal improvements. New crops or new varieties often prove susceptible to diseases or insect pests that were not previously a problem. New methods of control must then be devised. Similarly, new control methods permit the growing of crops or varieties not previously successful. Changes in individual crops open up new possibilities for crop combinations, as when earlier maturity of one crop permits a new succeeding crop to be introduced, or a higher yield from a feed crop permits the raising of more livestock. Here again there are almost unlimited possibilities of crop and livestock combinations to be tried and developed.

It is too often assumed that the future agriculture of a region already under cultivation must always remain much like the present one except for changes in detail. Actually, very big changes may be possible. The pattern of cropping can change dramatically. Soil fertility can be markedly increased. New implements and power sources can transform farm practices. Farms can change in size. Productivity can sometimes be increased severalfold.

None of these will change the basic nature of the agricultural process: utilizing the energy of the sun through the growth of plants, and of plant products through the growth of livestock.

This process can be increased in efficiency almost indefinitely. To do that, its special features—including its differences from factory production—must be recognized, honored, and used with intelligence, imagination, and hard work.

24

CHAPTER 2

The Farmer

The basic difference between native vegetation and wild animal life on the one hand, and agriculture on the other, is the presence of a *farmer*. The energy of the sun hits the surface of the earth everywhere, whether any human being is present or not. Wherever the temperature is right and moisture is present, plants grow and animals live. It is man who takes control of this situation, learning to use the products of plant and animal life, modifying plants and animals and the nature of the soil to serve his purposes better, and the man who does this is the farmer.

In the operation of his farm, each farmer plays two roles. He is at the same time a cultivator and a manager.

The Farmer As a Cultivator

The first role of each farmer is to take care of plants and animals in order to get useful products. With respect to plant growth, this includes the preparation of a seedbed, the sowing of the crop, the elimination of weeds, the management of soil moisture, and measures for the control of pests and diseases. With respect to animal growth, it includes controlling the breeding of livestock, herding and feeding them, protecting them from diseases, and, where necessary, housing them.

Some of these tasks are part of even primitive cultivation, while others are added step by step as farmers progress toward the establishment of modern farms. Not only are new tasks of cultivation added

25

as agriculture develops, such as the placement of fertilizer, the more careful application of irrigation water, and the application of insecticides and pesticides, but farmers have to learn to do the old operations of plowing, seeding and weed control in new ways.

The Farmer As a Manager

The other role of the farmer with respect to the farm he operates is to be a manager. Whereas the skills of cultivation are mostly skills of the hand, the muscles, and the eye, the skills of management involve activities of the mind backed up by the will. They involve primarily the making of decisions, or choices between alternatives.

The decisions each farmer must make as a manager include choosing between different crops that might be planted in each field, choosing what livestock are to be kept on the farm, and deciding how to distribute available labor time among different tasks, especially at times of the year when several different tasks need to be carried out at the same time. They include choices as to what and how many draft animals are to be kept for work in the fields.

As agriculture progresses, the farmer must develop more and more skills in buying and selling. He must decide whether or not he will purchase improved seeds, fertilizers, insecticides, or new implements. He must decide whether or not to employ additional laborers to work in the fields. He must decide how much of each crop is to be kept for home consumption and how much is to be sold. He must decide when to sell his products and to whom to sell them.

The managerial tasks of buying and selling are not a part of the role of the farmer in a wholly subsistence agriculture where no supplies are purchased and where all of the products are consumed by the farm family. But agricultural development depends on farms becoming more "commercial," with more and more purchases of production supplies and equipment, and more and more sales of products in the market.

The managerial tasks of farmers are made more difficult by the great variety of local soils and climatic conditions mentioned in the preceding chapter. If the soils of each farm in a region were just like the soils of all other farms in the region, if the slope of the land were the same and the effect of the sun were the same on lands sloping in

26

Mechanic

Manager

Bookkeeper

Buyer

FACTORY

Salesman

In factory production different persons perform specialized services.

FARMER:

Cultivator   Manager   Bookkeeper   Buyer   Seller

Most farm operators must perform all functions.

27

different directions, then it would be possible to develop standard "recipes" for the most productive use of each field, and each farmer could be supplied with instructions from some expert as to what he should do and how and when he should do it. But in the real world of widely varying agricultural conditions even within short distances, including differences in local prices of farm supplies and farm products, most of the managerial choices about the operation of each farm must be made by the operator of that farm.

Consequently, it is important to agricultural development that farmers grow in managerial ability so that they may competently take advantage of every opportunity open to them, each to make his farm as productive as possible, with an increasing margin between the costs and the returns of his farming operations.

The Farmer As a Person

The farmer is more than a cultivator and a manager. He is a *person* and a member of two groups of persons that are important to him. He is a member of a *family* and he is a member of a *local community* or neighborhood. Much of what the farmer is as a person he owes to his membership in these two social groups. Much of what he can do as an individual is determined by them.

As persons, farmers have four capacities of importance to agricultural development: to work, to learn, to think imaginatively and creatively, and to aspire. It is each farmer's ability to work and to learn, at least to the extent of mastering the skills of cultivation practiced by his father, that enables him to be the cultivator and the manager of a farm.

It is the farmer's capacity to learn new techniques and master new knowledge beyond that possessed by his father that makes it possible for him to change his methods so that agriculture becomes more productive. It is their capacity to imagine and create that enables some farmers to find entirely new and more productive ways to operate their farms.

To aspire, to long for something better than one has or is, can be a powerful stimulant under certain conditions.

First, a person must have a vision of a better way of life that he believes is possible for him. Second, to keep this aspiration alive and

28

Many farmers get a feeling of pride and satisfaction out of doing their work well and even out of farming more successfully than their neighbors.

make it a powerful drive, he must make enough progress toward the goal that he feels it worthwhile to keep striving.

It is easy to make the mistake of thinking rural people do not really want a better life just because their aspirations seem modest. But rural people in poor countries are not alone in this. Few of us "ask for the moon"; what we aspire to is a little improvement over what we have, or are, at the present time.

Characteristics of Farmers

Think, for a few minutes, about three farmers you know. Include one that you consider progressive and one you consider backward. Ask yourself *why* each one of them works (if he does). Ask yourself what, to your knowledge, each has learned in the past year. *Why,* in your opinion, has he learned that? So far as you know, has any one of them developed a new way of doing something on his farm? To what does each of them aspire? What does he want or hope for from life?

It would be better to do this for twenty farmers than for three, to insure a more realistic variety of persons, but three should illustrate what we are trying to examine here.

From this exercise, you can probably draw certain conclusions about farmers as persons.

Farmers vary enormously as persons. Most of them work pretty hard. They learn a little, but not much, from year to year. They seldom develop new methods; for the most part they use the methods of their fathers and occasionally pick up a new one from neighbors. What they hope for from life may be a modest improvement on the past, or it may be simply that they be spared from hunger, illness, and the death of their children. They hope that they can keep the land they have or even that they can get a little more.

Meanwhile there are some farmers (usually few) who actively reach out for new methods, learn quite a bit from year to year, and look forward to a much better future.

There are also some who seem not able to keep up at all. They let the weeds grow and the livestock wander. They fall further and further into debt. They have lost hope and they may lose their land.

Most farmers (like the rest of us) live far below their capacities. This is the second conclusion you probably can draw from thinking about farmers you know. They could learn much more than they do, if they had the opportunity and encouragement. They could try out more new methods than they do. Only a few of them are stupid, but almost all of them live largely by habit. They learn to do something in a particular way and keep on doing it that way, year after year.

This living by habit is not peculiar to farmers. We all do it. To a certain extent we all must do it. Habits are of enormous value. They free us from consciously thinking about the basic tasks of walking and talking and the simple manual operations of plowing, sowing and eating that are so much of the activity of everyday life. They free our minds for more important tasks.

Three mental habits are particularly important to agricultural (and all other kinds of) development. One is the habit of measuring; thinking in terms of amounts of things. This habit leads a person, in looking at a harvest, not to be satisfied with considering it a "good" harvest but to ask exactly how good it is in terms of kilograms, maunds, or bushels per hectare, bigha, or acre. The second useful mental habit is that of always asking why. Why is this crop better than that? Why is this field less fertile than that? The third is the habit of constantly looking for alternatives, for other ways of doing anything one has to do. Always considering alternatives can become as much of a habit as always doing something in the same way.

But habits can also be a nuisance and an obstacle. They make it difficult to learn new ways of doing old tasks. They make it difficult to consider new methods. Persons frequently come to consider their habitual behavior as an essential part of being themselves and feel they are traitors to themselves if they shift to a method suggested by someone else. All of us do this to some extent.

Habit is like friction in the physical world. Whether it is an asset or a liability depends on what is being attempted at the moment. Friction is an asset in the brakes of a bicycle or automobile, it is a liability between the moving parts of a pump or engine. With respect to agriculture, habit is an asset in carrying forward activities that have previously been learned, but it can be a liability with respect to the learning of new techniques.

But our main point here is that most farmers live far below their capacities as persons, and one of the tasks of agricultural development is to help them, and make it easier for them, to develop as persons so that they regularly use much more of each of the capacities they have.

The third conclusion you can draw from thinking about your farmer friends is really a group of conclusions about *why they do the things they do, and are the way they are.*

Here we cannot generalize very much and readers in different parts of the world will come to somewhat different conclusions because of the different societies (cultures) in which they and their farmer friends live. Consequently, we shall state only tentative generalizations here, in the form of questions for each reader to answer for himself.

Is it not true that farmers farm for what they, themselves and their families, can get out of it either in goods or in personal satisfaction? Very few of them have any sentimental attachment to cultivation for the sake of cultivation. Some of them genuinely "love the

31

land," but they want more from cultivating it than pleasant exercise in a favorite setting. What all farmers want is food and fiber and money with which to buy other commodities for family use. They want family security. They may in addition (and many of them do) get a feeling of pride and satisfaction out of doing their work well and even out of farming more successfully than their neighbors. They may get even more satisfaction if their achievements are recognized by others in the local community.

Is it not true that farmers are so aware of uncertainties of the weather and of prices that they are reluctant to try a new method unless they are sure it will succeed? Much of the "conservatism" of farmers is pure shrewdness. They are too smart to take chances, particularly if they have few savings, have small farms, and live near the margin of subsistence. To overcome this wise conservatism any new method proposed must promise very substantial increased returns.

Is it not true that most farmers place a high value on the good will and approval of their families and neighbors? Money is not everything. Friendship and social approval are important to most of us. We fear ridicule and we fear being shut out from the companionship of our fellows even more. Farmers share these feelings. Their behavior reflects this. Part of the task of agricultural development is to take measures that shift the climate of social opinion from respecting those farmers who farm in the same old way to honoring those who climb to higher productivity through changing their methods even when this involves risky experimentation.

Is it not true that the most progressive farmers are those who have the most confidence in their own judgment and who may feel less personal need for the approval of others? They are less fearful of ridicule because they are sure that even if they make a mistake they can correct it and succeed the next time, or the next. Such persons become the pioneers, the "innovators" in each society. While they seem to have less regard for the immediate approval of friends or neighbors, they are not unaware of it. They simply have confidence that *in the long run* they will succeed and gain this approval. Whether they actually receive approval in their lifetime or not, the progressive development of each society is actually led by, and built upon,

32

"Is it not true that most farmers place a high value on the good will and approval of their families?"

the accomplishments of such persons.

Is it not true that farmers resent being pushed around and told what to do? All of us do. Farmers want to be treated as human beings, as persons, as intelligent, responsible persons. They can accept help and advice from others only to the extent that doing so does not violate their own self-respect and their own integrity as persons.

The Influence of the Family

We have spoken of the farmer as being the one who tends crops and livestock and makes the decisions about what is to be grown and the methods to be employed. It might be more accurate to say that decisions are made by the farm family, since the various farming operations are carried on by different members of the family. The ways in which farm tasks are shared vary from one culture to another. In some places, men cultivate the crops; in other places their wives do this. Sometimes it is the men who take products to market; in other

33

cultures it is the women. In many rural societies the men do the field work but their wives manage the family's money. Where this is the practice, women have a considerable influence on how much is to be spent for such items as fertilizers, insecticides, and implements.

Sons also may have considerable influence on their fathers. Young people tend to be attracted to new ideas and to new ways of doing things. Why is this? Do they recognize new ways as opportunities at a time when they are still growing up and when they are free to experiment without risking their reputations as adults? Is it simply that they have not yet failed often enough to become cautious? In some cultures, sons frequently urge their fathers to adopt improved methods, even threatening to leave the farm for the city unless more modern methods are adopted.

The affection of husbands and fathers for their families makes them eager to obtain for their families some of the better things of life of which they have become aware. Today millions of fathers in rural parts of the world want more education for their children and are willing to work hard and to adopt improved methods of farming to make this possible. Where medical facilities have become available, they want their families to have the benefit of these. Where they have become acquainted with ways of making their home more comfortable, they want these for their families. Where new products such as flashlights, bicycles, shoes and even cosmetics have become available in local bazaars, these also are stimuli to families to raise their production so that they can increase their purchases.

It is these considerations bearing on the possibility of new amenities and comforts of rural living that give importance to extension educational programs for women, and to youth clubs related to agricultural production and to home life. These educational activities increase the incentives of farm people to make their farms more productive.

Most of the decisions with respect to agriculture are still made by the farmer as an individual. But he makes these decisions in the light of his membership in a family, his desire to do what he can for other members of the family group, and the influence which other members of the family have on him. Being dependent on the produce of the farm for a livelihood, other members of his family may bring

34

pressure on the farmer to make this or that decision, or to adopt this or that practice. On the other hand, the desire of the farmer to secure a better level of living for his family is an effective pressure on him in many circumstances to improve the productivity of the farm business.

Community Influences

Farmers' decisions are likewise greatly influenced by attitudes and relationships within the local communities in which they live. To a farmer, his community means many things. It is his chief source of security. He relies upon his friends and neighbors to help him in emergency, or to aid his family if anything happens to him. Members of rural communities commonly cooperate to do things that would be difficult or impossible for individuals working alone—clearing new land, or operating local irrigation facilities. Because of this mutual dependence, farmers are usually reluctant to do anything that would upset the community structure or break down traditions of mutual aid.

It is largely on his community that a farmer must depend for social approval. Community traditions define what sorts of conduct are "proper" for each person. They define the actions an individual may undertake on his own and those for which he should first obtain community consent.

There is considerable variation around the world in the social values and traditions of rural communities. In each place—and at each time—these reflect adjustments to the conditions under which the group has lived in former generations. Where agriculture is still primitive and where the fear of natural catastrophe is always present, traditions are usually designed more to protect the group against famine or other disaster than to encourage experimentation with new ideas and new techniques of production. Where the technology of agriculture has begun to change, however, and people have begun to enjoy increased production through the adoption of new practices, the traditions and social values shift towards attaching higher value to individual experimentation and the introduction of still more new methods.

We have compared habits of human behavior to friction in the natural world. Similarly, the influence of tradition and social values can be compared to the pull of gravity in a hilly country. Traditions and social values that have grown up largely in a static society with a primitive agriculture are like an uphill slope facing the person within the group who has a desire to experiment with new methods. He has to plod uphill *against* the power of the values of the group of which he is a part if he wishes to advance. On the other hand, other sets of traditions and social values that grow up in communities where the values of progress have been learned are like a downhill slope for the person who wishes to try new ways. The community is "with him" in his efforts. It respects his experimentation. It honors his achievements and this makes it far easier for the person who has a new idea or wishes to try a new method to proceed with his experimentation.

People's belief in these values and traditions must be recognized and respected. But the values and traditions themselves should not be considered immovable obstacles to development. They change over time, and development is itself an instrument in changing them. As the benefits of development become clear they demonstrate that those traditions and social values that obstruct progress have become outmoded.

The "Great Traditions" and Religion

Beyond the social values and traditions of local communities, yet affecting them in varying degree, are what Robert Redfield has called the "Great Traditions." These are the living philosophies formulated by the great thinkers, teachers, and prophets of society. They, too, have an effect on the behavior of farmers as persons, in addition to the influences of family and local community.

Basic beliefs about life and its meaning color the attitudes and actions of great numbers of people throughout wide regions. Is life on earth real, or is it but an illusion from which it should be man's chief goal to obtain release? Is human striving meaningful, or is it but an empty round of futile activity? Is progress truly possible, or is history but the account of ceaseless change? Has man the right to use other forms of life for his own purposes, or do plants or animals have rights to life that it is sinful for man to violate? May loans be made at interest, or is this contrary to moral law? Are human beings of ultimate value in themselves, or are they merely creatures of society to be used as society—or the state—may choose? Do all things come to him who waits, or does God help those who help themselves?

It is not our purpose here to argue these questions one way or another, but only to point out that people's beliefs about such things inevitably affect what they believe is possible and what they believe is worthwhile, what they believe they *may* do and what they believe they *must* do, and how they do it. These outlooks upon life affect the behavior not only of farmers but of all of us—scientists, teachers, legislators, planners.

Such basic beliefs change only slowly, but even they change over time—if not in fundamentals, at least in the way they are applied to different situations.

––––––––––

The farmer plays a pivotal role in agricultural development. It is he who tends crops and livestock and makes decisions about how his farm is to be used. It is he who must learn and adopt the new methods that are necessary to make farming more productive.

Farmers, as persons, behave basically in the same ways as all other human beings. They have the same inherent capacities and they are motivated by similar personal drives and social influences. Their actions are influenced by their families, by their friends and neighbors, and by the Great Traditions of the cultures in which they live.

The social values and traditions of rural communities and of the larger societies of which they are part in some ways help and in some ways hinder agricultural development. Generally, as new agricultural practices prove their worth the idea of trying out new methods in order to increase production gains increasing social acceptance.

The Farm

A farm is a portion of the earth's surface on which a particular farmer, farm family, or other organization cultivates crops or tends livestock. It is *land*.

Nature determined the basic character of the soil and its exposure to sunlight, the amount and seasonal distribution of rainfall, the lengths of days and nights, the air temperatures, and other physical features.

The character of the land is also affected by what men have done to it in the past. They may have increased the productivity of the soil by good management. They may have increased the control over soil moisture by irrigation or drainage, or by modifying the nature of the soil itself. They may have changed the slope of the land by grading or terracing.

In addition to the land itself, a farm may include structures erected on the land: wells, irrigation channels, fences to control livestock or to keep out wild animals, buildings to house livestock or to protect equipment or to store farm produce, a house in which the farmer and his family live, and perhaps houses for hired laborers.

The Farm and Agricultural Development

From the standpoint of agricultural development, the most important point about farms is that they need to change, both in size and in arrangement, in order to make it possible to utilize changing methods of farming more efficiently. The types of farms that are appropriate primitive agriculture are not the types that are most productive when modern methods are available.

Shifting cultivation. One primitive type of farm is that associated with shifting, or "slash-and-burn" cultivation: cutting the trees and burning them so that a crop can be planted, usually without plowing.

This type of cultivation arises where land has been in forests, usually in the tropics, and where soil fertility declines rapidly under cultivation. A family clears one or more plots sufficiently to make it possible to plant a crop. After a few seasons, as soil fertility declines and weeds increase, these plots are abandoned and new ones are cleared and planted. The family's claim to the land results from its having cleared it, and ceases as soon as the plots are no longer cultivated.

Shifting cultivation is low on the scale of agricultural development. When man learns how to manage that particular soil so that continuous cropping become economically feasible, the shifting ceases and the agriculture becomes settled.

Settled agriculture. The other primitive type of farm arises where the native soil is more fertile and retains its fertility at an acceptable level under continuous cropping. Here farms are settled permanently and the same fields cultivated year after year, perhaps with certain fields left fallow periodically to allow the land to rest and regain some of its former fertility.

Private field cultivation and "common" grazing lands. While shifting cultivation is carried on almost exclusively by human labor, primitive settled agriculture usually begins to utilize draft animals for some of the heavier field operations. These animals must be fed, and grazing is the simplest way of feeding them. To make this possible, some of the land must be left in grass.

In the beginning, before all of the land is wanted for cultivation, domesticated livestock, whether for draft or for meat, milk, wool or hides, can be grazed on the land not yet under cultivation. As population increases and more and more land is wanted for cultivation, many communities set aside certain areas for grazing. This gives rise to the combination of private field cultivation and "common" grazing lands: grasslands available for grazing by all of the livestock owned by anyone in the community.

This answer to the need for grazing lands is satisfactory in the beginning. But as the numbers of livestock increase, and as scientific methods of animal breeding and feeding, and scientific methods of raising the productivity of grasslands become available, it stands in the way of further agricultural development. "What is everyone's business is no one's business." Everyone has the right to use the common pastureland but no one has the responsibility to take care of it and improve the efficiency of its use.

Scattered fields. The fields that, taken together, make up a farm need not all be in one place. In the beginning, a farmer may lay claim to different plots in different places, selecting the most fertile plots not already being cultivated by someone else. Even after all land is being cultivated, communities frequently allot plots in different parts of the total land available to the community to a particular farmer since different plots have different levels of fertility and are suitable for different crops. This can give everyone some of the better and some of the poorer land, and allow each family to come closer to producing the variety of crops it needs and wants.

Here, again, needs change as new methods of farming become

A farm includes the improvements on the land like these terraces in Indonesia.

available. If new implements work better on larger fields, the farmer with all of his land in one place has more opportunity to change the size and shape of individual fields than does the farmer whose fields are scattered. Irrigation, and pest and disease control, likewise, are made easier by having all of the land of each farm in one bloc.

Legal rights in land. In the beginning, the right of a farmer to continued use of his farm is based on tribal or community custom. It is his because he cleared it, or because he has been cultivating it continuously, and it remains his as long as he uses it.

When the population of a settled agricultural community increases to the point where the fertile land is all being used, a family without land but wanting some, or a farmer who wishes to enlarge his farm, must either buy the "ownership," or rent the temporary use of land to which someone else has had the rights.

Once land becomes valuable, complex customs and laws develop regarding its ownership, sale, rental, and inheritance. These differ from country to country and even within countries. They vitally affect the freedom and the willingness of farmers to adopt and use the most efficient methods of farming currently available. They may increase this freedom and willingness or they may decrease it.

Toward More Efficient Farms

Five kinds of government action may be necessary to assure farmers effective control of their land and to enable them to farm more efficiently: (1) survey of the land and registration of ownership titles, (2) enclosure of land to eliminate indiscriminate grazing, (3) consolidation of scattered land holdings, (4) redistribution of land to provide management units of efficient size, and (5) change of the conditions of tenancy.

Land survey and titles. The first need is the clear demarcation of farm boundaries and the registration of land titles. Raising the productivity of agriculture involves making investments in the land itself. One cannot expect farm operators to make such investments unless they are sure of their right either to keep the land or to be repaid for the effort and expense that they put into improving it. Moreover, any change in the system of land tenure requires first a knowledge of who has what rights at the present time. Consequently, wher-

Shifting cultivation in Sarawak

Settled agriculture in Indonesia

43

ever there has not already been a land survey that clearly shows farm boundaries, and registration of land titles, this needs to be undertaken.

Enclosure. Combining crops with livestock by using certain fields of a farm for grazing is an efficient pattern of production for farmers in many areas. This is quite different, however, from the pattern in which farmers grow crops in their own fields but graze livestock on lands owned by the village "in common," with these grazing lands frequently scattered among cultivated fields and not separated from them by fences.

Grazing-lands-in-common are a serious hindrance to efficient crop cultivation and a barrier to progressive management of livestock. In the first place, it is hard to keep the livestock on the commons and out of adjacent cultivated fields. Literally millions of people, mostly women and children, spend their days herding livestock and trying to keep them where they belong—seldom with complete success. Second, most common lands, particularly in densely populated areas, are grazed by too many animals. The grass is kept too short to grow well; the better quality grasses die out entirely. Because the land is free to all, no one has an individual incentive to limit the number of animals he turns on to it or otherwise to protect and maintain it. Finally, progressive farmers who want to improve their own animals cannot do so as long as their stock grazes together with that of others on the common land. They cannot control diseases, nor can they control breeding so as to improve their herds.

Enclosure means putting an end to such indiscriminate grazing of common lands. There are several ways of doing this. Where the common lands are suitable for crop production, they may be made into individually owned farms. Where their best use is for grazing, they may likewise be sold to individual farmers, subject to restrictions against misuse—for example, against plowing or overgrazing lands so steep as to be subject to destructive erosion.

If the lands are kept in common ownership, the community must undertake active management of them. The first necessary step is

Scattered common grazing lands en- courage overgrazing and poor live- stock management.

44

Common Grazing Land

Common Grazing Land

Common Grazing Land

to fence the lands. This can end the straying of livestock into cultivated fields. Once the common lands have been fenced, overgrazing can be prevented by limiting the number of livestock allowed on them. Each owner of livestock can be charged a fee for each animal he is permitted to turn onto the lands. The funds received can be used to pay the costs of managing and maintaining the lands. This makes the owners of livestock bear the costs of grazing them. But it still does nothing about the problem of disease control and selective breeding.

Some Indian communities in Peru have adopted another solution to the problem of common grazing. The sheep flock in each village is organized cooperatively. It is managed by one person, with the villagers sharing in costs and returns in proportion to the share of each in the flock. In addition, improved breeding stock is being introduced.

Enclosure is bitterly opposed by many people because it changes the traditional rights in the common lands. An educational program to help people understand the benefit of enclosure to the whole community is usually necessary to overcome such opposition.

Consolidation of holdings. Fragmented holdings can be inefficient to operate. It is hard for a family to protect all its scattered plots from stray animals—or from pilfering neighbors. A farmer cannot install an irrigation well that will serve his whole farm. He gets little benefit from using insecticides and fungicides unless owners of adjacent plots also use them, and all at the same time. He is deterred from buying implements that would be burdensome to carry back and forth to his several fields. He has no flexibility for altering the size or shape of individual fields in case this is needed to take advantage of new methods of cultivation.

How serious an obstacle fragmentation is to agricultural development in an area must be judged in the light of local conditions. Where it is a serious problem, consolidation of holdings can greatly facilitate development.

Consolidation, like enclosure, is difficult, partly because most farmers feel an attachment to the fields they have been accustomed to cultivating, but more because they fear that in the redistribution of land the farm they receive may not be as productive as the one they have had before. Also, where different parts of the land around

"Fragmented holdings can be inefficient to operate."

a village are suited to different crops, farmers fear that they may have to change the crops they are accustomed to growing.

Land redistribution. Some farms are so large that they are not used intensively by their owners. Frequently the size of the farm confers more prestige on its owner than does his efficiency in operating it. He may be satisfied with the income from using only part of his land. He may be more interested in the social power that goes with land-holding than in the income from farming it. He may rent parts of it out to many tenants on terms that give them little incentive to use the land intensively. Similarly, where large plantations, even though efficiently operated and highly productive, are owned by foreigners, there is likely to be considerable pressure to confiscate the land and divide it into a larger number of smaller farms, each operated by a citizen of the country.

The pressure to break up large land holdings and to transfer ownership to the operators of the smaller farms is usually more political than economic. Political as well as economic power goes with land

47

ownership. Breaking up large estates into many owner-operator farms thus redistributes political power as much as it changes economic opportunity.

But the pressures for land redistribution are economic and psychological also. Almost every farm family would prefer to own the land it farms. Ownership gives the farm family a feeling of security. The land is theirs. They have a continuing right to live on it and use it as long as they wish, provided only that they pay their taxes. Ownership also increases the opportunity of each farmer to farm as he pleases without having to take account of the wishes (or orders) of a landlord.

From the standpoint of efficiency in farming, the most productive size of individual farms varies from place to place within any one country, and it keeps changing from year to year with changes in available methods of farming and with changes in the relative cost of land, of labor, and of the supplies and equipment currently used in producing crops and livestock.

There is no one answer to the question of how big, or small, farms should be for maximum productivity. The most productive situation is usually one in which the farms in a country are of many different sizes and these sizes keep changing gradually in response to technical progress and economic development. Land redistribution, therefore, is a complicated question and one that needs separate and deep study in each country. It *can* substantially accelerate agricultural development. It can do this through its effect on the incentives of individual farm operators to apply all available methods of increasing production on land that is theirs. It can do it by its effect on the distribution of political power. It can do it by its adjustment of farm size to the most productive systems of farming and to prevailing cost relationships among land, labor, and supplies and equipment. But land redistribution can also retard development by dividing it into too many farms, each of them too small for efficient management.

The positive contribution of land redistribution to accelerating agricultural development usually occurs only after some time. The first consequence frequently is a lowering of production, particularly where cultivators who have not previously been managing farms become farm operators.

Changing the conditions of tenancy. Although ownership of the land they cultivate is the goal of most farmers, tenancy can play a constructive role in agricultural development. It can be a way of making land available to skillful farmers who lack the money to buy enough land for efficient farming. It allows such a farmer to put his own money, or the funds he can borrow, into implements, tools, draft animals, fertilizer, improved seeds and other supplies without also having to go into debt to pay for the land. For tenancy to be satisfactory, however, it must (1) involve a reasonable rental and (2) insure security of tenure. It is better, in addition, if it leaves management decisions about the farm business largely in the hands of the tenant.

After all, even "owning" land seldom carries with it complete freedom for the owner to use the land entirely as he wishes. It is doubtful that it should. Society has an interest in seeing both that the land is used efficiently and that its fertility is conserved and improved for future generations. Society therefore sets "the rules of the game" within which each farmer operates the land of his farm. Sometimes these rights involve ownership within certain legal restrictions. Sometimes they are rights of tenancy, again subject to laws and regulations that encourage efficiency, conservation, and land improvement from generation to generation. There are cases when the need is not for redistribution of the land itself among farms but for a revision only of the rights of ownership and of tenancy to stimulate greater efficiency in use of the land. Reform of the conditions of tenancy holds real possibilities for speeding development in some countries where redistribution of ownership is still some distance in the future.

A farm, then, may be described as a place, a portion of the earth's surface, where agriculture is carried on by a particular farmer whether he be owner, tenant, or employed manager. It consists of those resources for agricultural production that are found in that place: the sunlight, the soil, the moisture; the improvements that have been made in the land; and the structures that have been built upon it.

The form, the arrangement and the size of farms need to be different in different parts of a country, depending on the local nature of the land and the type of cultivation for which it is best suited. These characteristics of farms need to change over time with changes in methods of farming if agriculture is to be most productive.

Society sets the rules within which individual farmers may use their farms. Part of agricultural development is to keep studying the influence of existing types and sizes of farms on productivity and to make appropriate changes in laws and tenancy contracts governing the use of land.

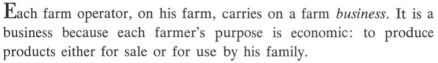

CHAPTER 4

The Farm Business

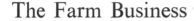

Each farm operator, on his farm, carries on a farm *business*. It is a business because each farmer's purpose is economic: to produce products either for sale or for use by his family.

This statement will be denied by many people. Many people say that "farming is not a business; it is a way of life." They say this particularly about primitive and subsistence agriculture. Their argument is that business is a matter of buying and selling but farming is a matter of sowing and reaping, depending on the processes of nature to bring about the harvest. They point out that for farmers and their families production is mixed up with consumption and work with recreation, as when those who take products to market and sit all day talking with neighbors and purchasers get as much enjoyment out of the process as profit from their sales.

This point of view is put forward even by many officials and planners who seem to prefer to believe that farmers do not respond to price changes, do not behave as businessmen, and can only be herded about like sheep, by orders and regulations.

It is true that farming *is* a way of life, that production *is* mixed up with consumption, that social satisfactions *are* built into the way farmers of many societies go about their daily tasks.

At the same time, it is important to recognize that farming is a *business* insofar as production is concerned. To realize this it is necessary only to get acquainted with farmers and observe what causes them to change crops or methods. Farming involves more and more buying and selling as agricultural development proceeds. But even in a largely subsistence agriculture the better farmers think like other businessmen and learning to think in this way is a part of development.

Inputs and Outputs

In technical language, farm production uses *inputs* to produce *outputs*. *Inputs* are all the things put into the production process: the use of the land, the labor of the farmer and his family and any workers he may hire, his mental effort in planning and managing, the seed for his crops and feed for his animals, fertilizers, insecticides and other supplies, tools and implements, and bullocks or tractors. All the things that go into agricultural production are inputs. The *outputs* are the crop and livestock products the farm produces.

Costs and Returns

These inputs and outputs involve *costs* and *returns*. In a primitive agriculture the chief cost is the effort—the hard work and the skill—of the farmer and his family. In a subsistence agriculture the chief return is the value of the products in providing the family's own living. As agriculture becomes more highly developed, more and more of the costs are cash costs and more and more of the returns are in money. Cash is paid out for production supplies and equipment, and sometimes for hired wage-labor and for rent of land. Money is received for products sold.

Every farmer thinks about cost and returns, however primitive or advanced his methods of farming may be. His consideration of costs always includes the effort he must put forth. He includes the cash cost of the equipment and supplies he uses. He makes allowances for risks of crop failure, for the possibility of low market prices at harvest time, and for uncertainty regarding the effectiveness of new methods he is considering adopting. He may also take into account the disapproval of family, friends, or neighbors for departing from established patterns of cultivation, or from social traditions of what it is "proper" for him to do. The returns he considers include food and other farm products used by his family, the money received for products sold, and the value of goods and services that may be ob-

52

tained by exchange with neighbors. He may in addition take into account his family's or his neighbors' admiration for his skill.

His calculation of returns does not include the portion of his crop that he must give to the landlord (to the farmer this is a cost). It does not include any part of the harvest that social custom may require him to share with his neighbors through feasting, or with relatives for whom he has no real affection—except as this may add to his social standing in the community or set up future obligations to him

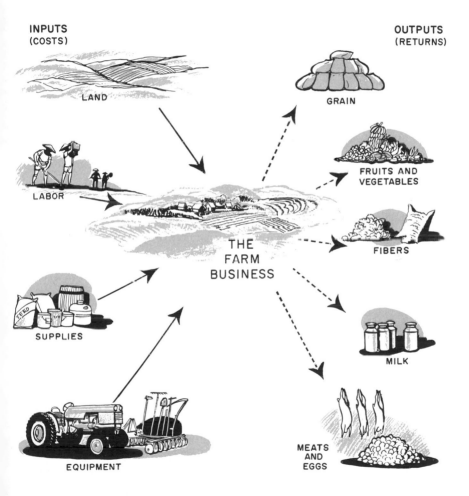

Farm production uses inputs to produce outputs. The inputs always include land and labor. For progressive agriculture they also include purchased supplies and equipment.

53

on their part. Nor does the farmer count as a "return" any surplus of production above his family's needs unless there is an available market in which he can sell it.

"Is it worth what it costs?" This question is constantly in each farmer's mind. His answer has great influence on what he does and what he does not do on his farm.

Farm Enterprises

Most farms produce a variety of products. In some areas, to be sure, the margin of returns over costs for one crop is so much greater than for any other that most farms throughout the area are planted almost entirely to that crop. But in most places the soil and climate, efficient use of labor, family need, and market conditions make it advantageous to each farmer to grow several different crops and often also to keep one or more kinds of livestock.

It is customary to speak of each of these different kinds of production as a farm "enterprise." Thus a farm business that combines the cultivation of maize, sugar-cane, wheat, and flax with the tending of poultry and milk cattle is said to include six farm enterprises.

Cropping Systems

A farmer cannot simply select individual enterprises for his farm business without considering them in relation to one another. Different crops have different growing seasons, make different demands on plant food nutrients from the soil, and require different amounts of attention at different times of the year.

Moreover, enterprise combinations are full of what economists call "joint products" and "joint costs." Wheat, grown for the grain, also produces straw that may be used for feeding or bedding livestock. Some of the fertilizer applied one year to a crop of wheat may remain in the soil to increase the yield of a sorghum crop in the following year. Fencing erected to control livestock so that better breeding practices may be followed may also protect growing crops from damage by straying animals. The manure from livestock may be used to fertilize cropland.

Consequently, the several enterprises included in a particular farm business are rarely separable in an accounting sense. Each farmer

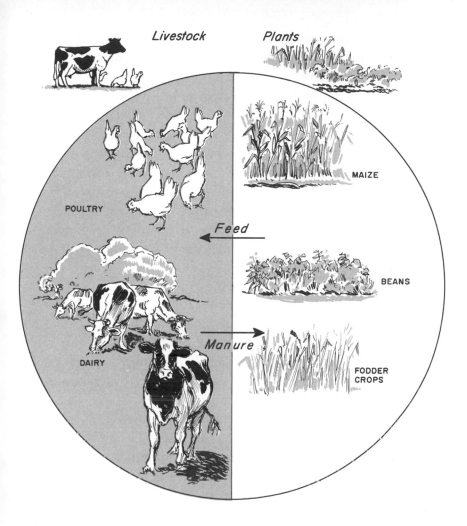

Livestock   Plants

POULTRY

MAIZE

Feed

BEANS

DAIRY   *Manure*

FODDER
CROPS

The Farm Business Is a Combination of Farm Enterprises
These enterprises:
1. Support each other.   2. Distribute labor requirements.
3. Jointly determine farm income.

tries to work out the best combination of crop and livestock enterprises for his own farm business, considering the land, labor and
other resources available to him.

Complexity of Each Farm Business

The discussion above should help to explain why it is that farm businesses vary so much, even in a single region. All farmers think in

terms of costs and returns but some of these are in money terms while others are related to the position and responsibilities of each farmer in his community. If the farm family consumes most of the products of its farm, its need for the foods in its customary diet and for other products of the farm will be the major factor in its choice of farm enterprises. To the extent that products are grown for sale, the choice of enterprises will be influenced by the accessibility of markets for different products and by their relative market prices.

A farmer's opportunity for off-farm employment may also influence how he uses his farm and what enterprises he chooses. He may find it advantageous to be less busy on his farm, in certain seasons or throughout the year, in order to supplement his income with wages earned elsewhere.

Difference Between Size of Farm and Size of Farm Business

The size of a farm in hectares is only one of several factors that determine the size of the farm business it supports. Another is the amount of labor applied to the various enterprises on the farm. Another is the amount of supplies and equipment purchased to be used in the farming operations. "Intensive" crops are those like vegetables that require large amounts of labor, fertilizer, and, frequently, irrigation. "Extensive" crops are those like pasture grasses and some cereal crops that, when not irrigated, require less labor per hectare. The addition of one or more livestock enterprises, particularly where most of the feed is purchased, can considerably increase the size of the farm business on a given area of land.

Consequently, a large farm may support a relatively small farm business if it is devoted only to extensive crops and pasture, or if some of it is not used at all. Likewise, a relatively large farm business can be developed on a small farm by combining several intensive crop and livestock enterprises on it.

Imagine four rice farms, each one hectare in size. On Farm A a mediocre local strain of rice is sown broadcast, no fertilizer is used, and nothing is done about disease control. On Farm B an improved variety of rice is grown, seedlings are carefully transplanted with proper regard for spacing, fertilizer is used, and modern methods are applied for disease control. On Farm C rice is grown in the same

56

FARM A

FARM B

FARM C

FARM D

"All four of these farms are of the same size (one hectare) but the farm businesses are all different in size." See explanation on pages 56-7.

57

way as on Farm B, but in addition fish are introduced into the flooded rice fields and later are caught for use as food. On Farm D all of the land is put into rice except for one plot, perhaps 30 by 75 feet in area. On this plot the farmer has built pens for growing chickens and he has a batch of broilers ready to market every two weeks.

All four of these *farms* are of the same size (one hectare), but the *farm businesses* are all different in size. The farm business on Farm B is larger than on Farm A, that on Farm C is larger than on Farm B, and that on Farm D is the largest of all.

It takes effort and imagination to develop a large farm business on a small farm but many farmers do it and many more could.

Implications for Agricultural Development

The fact that farming is a business has important implications for agricultural development.

Costs and returns are important. While the production process of farming is biological—the growth processes of plants and animals—the farmer is more interested in the relationship between costs and returns than he is in the physical size of the harvest alone.

Hence, with respect to each new farm practice and each new production input that is recommended to him a farmer very properly asks not only, "Will it be effective?" but, "Will it pay me to use it?"

Farmers think in terms of cropping systems. In considering whether or not to substitute one crop for another, each farmer considers how it will fit in with his other crops. If a new variety of rice promises a 15 percent increase in yield but requires a 20-day longer growing period, a farmer may reject it because it will prevent his getting the succeeding crop in on time. He may likewise continue to grow a crop that does not seem very profitable considered by itself provided it fits well into his cropping system.

Large farm businesses can be developed on small farms. It is possible to have relatively large farm businesses on relatively small farms by growing intensive crops or by raising poultry or swine or keeping dairy cattle (purchasing much of their feed). Considerable agricultural development can often be achieved by increasing the size of farm businesses without increasing the size of farms. This is important particularly for regions of small farms, dense population, and limited industrial employment opportunities.

Different types of farm businesses require different programs for development. Uniformity of development programs over a whole country may be attractive from the standpoint of ease of administration, but it is not the way to achieve the most rapid agricultural development. The wide variation in sizes of farms and types of cropping systems requires that the content of programs for development vary from locality to locality if they are to be most effective.

PART

II

The Essentials for
Agricultural Development

Agriculture gets its energy from the sun. It operates through the biological processes of plant and animal growth. It is managed by farmers who are human beings and members of families and of local communities. It is conducted on farms operated as businesses.

But agricultural development cannot be brought about by farmers acting alone. Agriculture cannot develop beyond the subsistence stage without appropriate developments in other parts of the life of the nation within which it is carried on.

In order for agricultural productivity to rise, each farmer depends more and more on resources from the outside. He supplements the plant food nutrients present in the soil with purchased fertilizers. He supplements soil moisture with irrigation water, frequently obtained through canals from sources far away. He sows purchased seed of

60

modified plants developed by specialized research organizations. He controls plant and animal diseases with chemicals and medicines manufactured in distant cities. He sells an increasing part of the produce of his farm to outside markets. Even the skills and knowledge which he applies in his farming are increased by education he receives in schools and sometimes colleges and through specialized extension services and other forms of adult education.

In Part II we consider five facilities and services that *must* be available to farmers if agriculture is to develop. Each of these is *essential*. Without any one of them there can be *no* agricultural development. With all of them there will be some, even in the absence of any of the "accelerators" discussed later in Part III.

These five essentials are:

Markets for Farm Products (Chapter 5)
Constantly Changing Technology (Chapter 6)
Local Availability of Supplies and Equipment (Chapter 7)
Production Incentives for Farmers (Chapter 8)
Transportation (Chapter 9)

Since all of these are essential, the order in which they are discussed here has no significance with respect to the importance of each.

(There are other ways in which agricultural development depends on the wider society in which it is found. Perhaps the most important of these is its dependence on the maintenance of law and order and the security of persons and property. This could rightly be listed as another "essential." It is not discussed in this book primarily because it is such a general requirement for all orderly human activity and development, and because there are no special requirements that agricultural development places upon it.)

61

CHAPTER 5

Markets for Farm Products

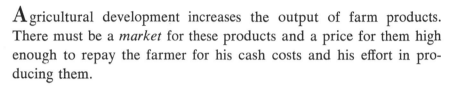

Agricultural development increases the output of farm products. There must be a *market* for these products and a price for them high enough to repay the farmer for his cash costs and his effort in producing them.

Three things are necessary:

1. Someone, somewhere who wants to buy farm products: there must be a *demand* for them.
2. Someone through whom to sell farm products: a *marketing system*.
3. *Farmers' confidence* in the working of the marketing system.

Domestic Demand

In only a few countries can there be sustained agricultural development without growth of a strong market demand for agricultural products within the country itself.

This is one of the ways in which agricultural and industrial development are dependent on each other. Industrialization depends upon agricultural development because industries must sell their products and farm people are an important part of the potential domestic market for them. Likewise, agricultural development depends upon industrial development because farmers need to be able to sell their surplus production to non-farm people and industrialization increases the number of non-farm wage earners.

The need for enlarging the domestic market for agricultural products is well exemplified by one country that, out of a population of 7,000,000 has only about 500,000 people—wage earners and their families living in cities—who form the off-farm domestic market for food produced on the farms. This country is well suited for the production of two crops for the international market: coffee and cotton. It already produces enough coffee to meet its marketing quota under international agreements. The cotton must compete with cotton exports from other countries. The country has large areas of good agricultural land not yet under cultivation, with fertile soils and adequate rainfall. Until there is considerable industrialization within the country, however, enlarging the domestic market for farm products, that country has relatively little opportunity for further agricultural development.

In contrast to this, it may be noted that during the period of the first rapid development of Japanese agriculture, there was a rapidly increasing demand for agricultural products within Japan.

DEMAND FOR AGRICULTURAL PRODUCTS
(Five Year Averages)
(In million yen)

Year	Domestic Demand
1878-82	420
1883-87	326
1888-92	463
1893-97	663
1898-02	1,058
1903-07	1,425
1908-12	1,754

Source: Tobata Seiichi and Ahkawa Kazushi (eds.), The Japanese Economy and Agriculture, Tokyo, Iwanami Shoten, 1956, Table 4.2.

There are a number of countries in which industrialization and urbanization have enlarged the domestic market for farm products, yet agricultural production within them has not developed to meet this increased demand. In some instances, this may be because it is more profitable to produce agricultural commodities for export and to import food. In most cases, however, there appear to be opportu-

64

Domestic demand is important for agricultural development. There must be many urban customers for farm products like the milk being sold in India (left) and the vegetables available on a street in Colombia (right).

nities for domestic agricultural development that are not being realized. The production of onions in Vietnam and of malting barley in Ecuador are examples of profitable replacement of imports by domestic production.

As more and more people are employed in the towns and cities, and as the incomes of many of them rise, they want not only to buy more food but better food—higher quality and higher priced foods— more fruits and vegetables and meats and milk, and new products that are tasty to eat and convenient to use. One often finds many processed foods in city stores and even in village markets in developing countries bearing labels that show that they have been imported. If someone had the initiative and know-how to produce them domestically this would provide both new industries for general economic development and an expanded market for increased farm production.

International Demand

If a country is particularly suited to grow a crop for which there is a strong international demand, this may provide the basis for consider-

65

able agricultural development. In many countries, agricultural exports make up a large part of total exports. They provide a substantial source of foreign exchange to buy machinery and other goods needed for industrial development. Rubber in Malaysia, rubber and tobacco in Indonesia, bananas in Ecuador, coffee in Brazil, sugar in the islands of the Caribbean, cocoa in Ghana and Nigeria, and animal products in New Zealand are examples.

Each country at early stages of the commercialization of agriculture should pay particular attention to opportunities to export agricultural products. Such countries need foreign exchange to pay for needed equipment and supplies, both for agricultural development and for industrialization. At the same time they also need to increase their food production for consumption within the country. In most cases, both can be done. But each case is unique and requires careful estimates of where the best balance between increasing food for domestic consumption and export products lies.

Development of the Marketing System

Few farmers can sell their own products in large city markets or abroad. These markets are too far away. An individual farmer, unless he is the operator of a very large plantation, has no way of contacting buyers in these markets. He does not have the means of transporting his products there. He does not have the know-how or the facilities for all the handling, packaging, storing, processing, and other operations that are involved. His volume of produce is not large enough to justify his performing these operations anyway; it would be inefficient for him to do so.

Most farmers must sell their products at the farm or in the local market. Their incentive to produce commodities for sale rather than only for their own subsistence therefore depends upon the prices they can get *locally*. These prices depend partly on the efficiency of the marketing system linking local markets to those in the city.

Marketing Functions

What constitutes an efficient marketing system, and how is one to be developed to meet the growing needs of a developing agriculture?

One function it must perform is *transportation:* products must be

66

moved, often hundreds or thousands of miles from the farms where they are produced to the cities where they are to be consumed or to seaports for export.

Another function is *storage*. Farm products become available at harvest time but consumers need to eat all year round. In a subsistence agriculture, farmers store their own crops. In a modern market economy this can be more efficiently done by marketing agencies using technically trained staff with well designed facilities and equipment to protect products from rat and insect infestation and other causes of deterioration and spoilage.

Perishable crops cannot be stored for long without *processing*. Plants for processing the seasonal surpluses of perishable crops therefore become important—drying, canning or tinning fruits, vegetables and meat products, and manufacturing cheese or dried or condensed milk. Processing opportunities are not limited to perishables, however. Most farm products are not eaten in the form in which they are produced. Rice must be milled and wheat ground into flour. Modern food technology permits the manufacture of many new products for which demands can be developed—packaged cereals, candies, beverages, and many others.

The development of transportation, storage, and processing facilities widens the market for farm products. Without them, there is a market only for what can be consumed at the time it is produced and close to the place where it is produced. With them, farmers have outlets for greater production, and for products that may be well suited for their farms but for which there would otherwise be too small a market to make them profitable.

Financing of marketing is another essential function. Farmers want to be paid when they deliver their products to the local buyer. It will be some time after that, however, before the final consumer pays for the processed products. Meanwhile, someone must finance the whole operation of grading, transporting, assembling, and processing until the final product is sold to the person who is to use it.

Finally, there is the task of *managing* the whole marketing operation. Those who assemble products in country market towns must have contacts in the city markets to which they ship. City buyers must have contacts with country sources of supplies. Processors must have sources of raw materials and outlets for their products. Arranging to get the right commodities to the right places at the right times and with a minimum of waste becomes an increasingly intricate task of market organization.

Costs of Marketing

No matter who performs the functions of marketing or how they are organized, each of the operations of marketing involves costs. Transportation costs money; storage costs money; processing costs money. The time and effort spent in studying demands and supplies, making trade contacts, selecting products, buying and selling them and directing their movements—this, too, is expensive.

Furthermore, a considerable investment is tied up in the products moving through the marketing system, and considerable risks are involved—risks of loss through spoilage or through price changes. A return must be paid on this invested capital just as on money that is loaned to farmers to enable them to buy seed, fertilizer, and other supplies.

MARKETING COSTS

Transportation
Storage
Labor Time
Investment
Risk
Spoilage
Credit
Maintaining Contacts
Information

TOTAL

"No matter who performs the functions of marketing or how they are organized, each of the operations of marketing involves costs."

The costliness of marketing often is not well understood by farmers or by consumers, or even by persons close to the marketing system itself. In a visit to a country grain market in India, a local official was asked what would be the most important thing that could be done to improve the market. Open piles of grain in the market were not graded. Much of the grain was contaminated by rat excreta, weed seeds and trash. A high percentage of the kernels had been damaged by weevils. The piles of grain were providing a feast for many birds. Yet the official did not mention the need for better handling methods or storage facilities. Instead, he recommended that the commission merchants in the market be done away with, since their function could be performed by the Market Commission "at no cost to the farmer."

In the absence of the present merchants *someone* would have to buy the grain, hold it, contact buyers in central markets, select the most advantageous outlet, and arrange for sale and shipment. In addition, someone should clean the grain, protect it from rats, insects and birds, and grade it properly. Costs and risks are involved for whoever performs these functions. Certainly a Market Commission could not do these things at no cost. Perhaps it could do them at less cost than private merchants. Or perhaps a producer's cooperative marketing association could do them more cheaply if it hired a skilled, industrious manager with a competent staff. Or perhaps more of the "middleman's profit" is made up of the inevitable costs of marketing than we usually realize. The present merchants may, or may not, be performing their function about as cheaply as anyone could.

Essential Governmental Activities

Whether a country's marketing system is operated by private merchants, by governmental agencies, or by cooperative societies, or by a combination of these, there are certain activities that the government itself should undertake. At the very least, the government must maintain a system of currency in which both merchants and farmers have confidence; it should establish standard weights and measures and regularly inspect the scales and other measuring devices used by merchants to see that they are correct; and it should provide for the legal enforcement of contracts.

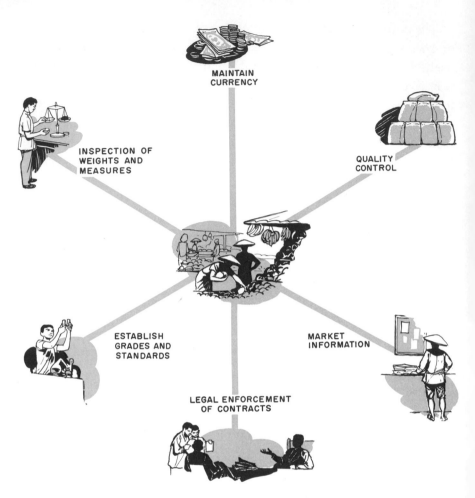

MAINTAIN
CURRENCY

INSPECTION OF
WEIGHTS AND
MEASURES

QUALITY
CONTROL

ESTABLISH
GRADES AND
STANDARDS

MARKET
INFORMATION

LEGAL ENFORCEMENT
OF CONTRACTS

Governmental services essential to marketing.

Another important task for the government is to set and enforce quality or grade standards for major agricultural commodities. There is not so much need for these where trade is only local, where buyers can inspect products personally before they buy them. Agricultural development, however, involves more and more trading between local and central markets. In this kind of trading, where personal inspection would be costly and time consuming, grades and standards provide a common language between buyers and sellers. They speed up trade and reduce risks and disputes. Quality standards help buyers obtain the kind of products best suited to their needs. They also provide a basis for paying higher prices to those producers who offer the qualities most in demand.

Governments can assist in guiding commodities in the right quantities to the right places at the right times, first of all, by assuring prompt and efficient postal service and telephone and telegraph service between local and central markets. In addition, a government can provide a market information service, independent of all marketing firms or agencies, in which public reports are made of shipments and receipts of commodities and of prices being paid for them in important market centers. If such reports are posted in local markets or announced over the radio, farmers are able to judge whether local prices fairly reflect market demands in the central markets. They no longer have to accept whatever is told them by local merchants about current prices. In addition, local shippers have a better basis for setting the prices they are willing to pay to farmers and for deciding where to consign their shipments for sale.

Private or Governmental Activities

The other functions of marketing—transportation, buying and selling, storage, grading, processing, and operating a banking system that provides both facilities for payment and access to short-term credit to finance marketing operations—may be performed in any of a variety of ways: private, governmental or cooperative.

One situation to be avoided is for any part of the marketing system to be allowed to become a monopoly of any one interest or organization without effective safeguards of the farmer's interest. It is customary to think of monopoly largely in connection with private merchants but cooperative societies or governmental agencies also may be monopolies. Monopoly is attractive to marketing agencies whether private, cooperative, or governmental. Each person or organization would like to keep the business to itself. Each can be efficient. But each is more likely to be efficient if it has to meet the standard of services, prices, and dependability of other persons or organizations offering to provide the same services within the marketing system.

Some monopoly is frequently unavoidable in marketing. Many local markets are not big enough for several buyers. Storage facilities are likely to be under single management. Here the need is for sufficient regulation of prices and of marketing services that the interests of farmers are protected.

Sometimes, too, there are many more middlemen than there need to be. In parts of Java grain passes through not one but a long succession of middlemen, many more than are needed. Even though most of the people involved make a poor living at it this is a costly method of marketing. Yet efforts to reduce the number have often faced the criticism that all of these middlemen have families who have to be supported. If a number of these middlemen are eliminated from the marketing system what will they do? This is a real problem, to be sure, but efficient and economical marketing is one of the essentials for agricultural development.

Recognition of the Importance of Marketing

In many countries, marketing and trade are looked down upon as an unworthy occupation. "Middlemen" who only "buy and sell what other men have produced" are despised as social parasites. The services they perform and the substantial costs that they bear are not taken into account. Where the work of buying and selling has been left largely to persons of another race and from another country—the Chinese in Southeast Asia, the Indians in East Africa, the Lebanese in West Africa—it has been too easy to underrate both the importance and the real costs of marketing. Since marketing operations are both essential and costly, it is important that they be done efficiently. The prices that can be paid to farmers are determined by the prices that final consumers are willing to pay minus the costs of marketing after the products leave the farm.

What is needed, first of all, is widespread understanding of the importance of marketing, of the knowledge and skill and willingness to take risks that are involved in doing it efficiently, and of the essential contribution that an efficient marketing system can make to agricultural development.

Farmers' Confidence in the Marketing System

Even where there is someone to sell *to* (market demand) and someone to sell *through* (a marketing system) these will not make their full

Farmers of the Lake Patzcuaro region of Mexico sell their eggs at a premium price in Mexico City because of the confidence buyers have in their grading and dependable fresh supply.

contribution to agricultural development unless farmers have confidence in the marketing system.

In a number of countries, even though farmers know that other crops, to be sold in the market, would be more profitable to them than crops they now grow for home consumption, they continue to use their fields for production of subsistence food crops. The reason frequently given is that the market is undependable. Farmers fear that if they shift to cash crops and, as a result, have to buy rice, sorghum or wheat for family consumption, the prices of these staple foods may rise to a point where it might be difficult or impossible for them to buy enough to feed their families.

There are several factors involved in developing farmers' confidence in the marketing system. One is a recognition and understanding by farmers of the essential services performed by merchants (private, cooperative, or governmental) and that each of these services has a legitimate cost. Another factor is the record of performance of the marketing system in the past. Still another is the degree of fluctuation of prices for different farm products and the predictability of these prices long enough ahead for farmers to make appropriate production decisions.

It is at this point that officially guaranteed prices for farm products probably have their most important effect. No matter what the level at which prices for individual farm products are guaranteed, if they are guaranteed for a considerable period into the future, farmers are in a far better position to plan their production, and much more ready to devote a larger part of their farms to producing crops for the market.

Processing plants for agricultural products can help here, too. They can offer a guaranteed price to farmers, thereby giving farmers confidence that they can dispose of increased production at known prices.

A final point to be emphasized is this: confidence is important not only to farmers, but to all those involved in the marketing system. Modern commerce depends upon the trust in each other of all the parties concerned, a trust supported by the knowledge that dishonesty is punishable by law. Such confidence is essential to efficient trade; development of it is an important part of developing an efficient marketing system.

CHAPTER 6

Constantly Changing Technology

Increased agricultural production comes from new techniques or methods put into practice on farms. It is simply not possible to get much increase by using the same old plant and animal materials and the same old soil in the same old ways.

The "technology" of farming means "the way it is done." It includes the methods by which farmers sow, cultivate, and harvest crops and care for livestock. It includes the seeds, the fertilizers, the pesticides, the medicines and the feeds they use, the tools, the implements and the sources of power. It includes enterprise combinations by which farmers seek to make the best use of their labor and land.

For agricultural development to proceed, these must constantly be changing. When they stop changing agriculture becomes stagnant. Production stops increasing and it may even decline due to decreasing soil fertility or to increasing damage by multiplying pests and diseases.

Limiting Factors

This does not mean that every practice, every item of farm supplies and equipment, and every implement and power source must change on each farm every year. Frequently much of the technology in use on a farm is capable of supporting higher production but production is being limited by only one or a few parts of this technology. Upgrading that one, or those few, can allow production to rise.

The Food and Agriculture Organization (FAO) has recently been sponsoring fertilizer trials on thousands of farms in many countries. In Turkey, the use of fertilizer in these trials raised wheat production by 52% and for each dollar spent on fertilizer the increased value of the harvest was $2.60. In Ghana, fertilizer increased the yield of groundnuts by 57% and each dollar spent on fertilizer increased the value of the harvest by $3.90. In Guatemala, fertilizer applied to cabbage raised the yield by 140%, and each dollar spent on the fertilizer increased the value of the harvest by $63.90.

These figures indicate, first, that fertilizer (a new technology) can raise agricultural productivity substantially and, second, that the other parts of farm technology where these trials were run were already adequate to support these higher yields. The varieties being used, the soil moisture available, and the prevailing techniques of cultivation were such that the fertilizer could be used effectively.

Other trials were less successful. For instance, in Syria fertilizer on unirrigated wheat raised the yield by only 22%, in comparison with 51% on irrigated wheat. Lack of moisture prevented the dryland wheat plants from taking full advantage of the fertilizer nutrients. In this instance, a lack of water as well as a lack of fertilizer was holding production down.

Such relative "failures" do not mean that fertilizer is not important but rather that it is not always the limiting factor. In some cases the soil already holds as much of the nutrient contained in the fertilizer as

The importance of local testing of new technology is emphasized in such programs as the FAO (Food and Agriculture Organization of the United Nations) fertilizer demonstrations in Nigeria (left) and small tools introductions in Ethiopia (right).

76

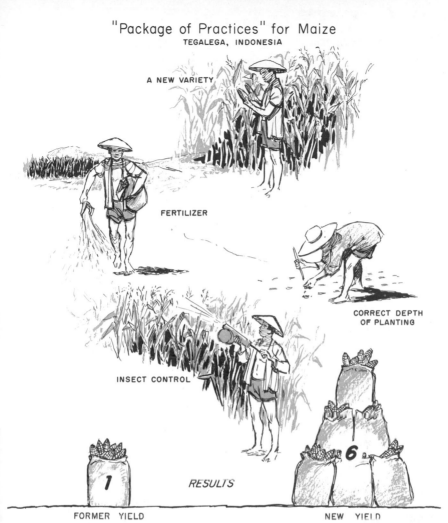

"Package of Practices" for Maize
TEGALEGA, INDONESIA

A NEW VARIETY

FERTILIZER

CORRECT DEPTH OF PLANTING

INSECT CONTROL

RESULTS

1

6

FORMER YIELD

NEW YIELD

the strains of crops currently being grown can utilize. For instance, in the Cauca Valley of Colombia, fertilizer on soybeans brought only a 16% increase in yields. Here the need may be for new crop varieties capable of utilizing more plant nutrients. As soon as such varieties are introduced it may then be found that the addition of fertilizers will be highly profitable.

"Packages" of Practices

Because of the intimate way in which different farm practices interact in affecting yields, it frequently is desirable to introduce several changes of technology simultaneously. In the village of Tegalega in

West Java, Indonesia, 57 farmers increased maize yields 600% (from 800 to nearly 5,000 kilograms per hectare) by (1) using a new variety, (2) using recommended amounts and kinds of fertilizer, (3) changing the depth of planting the seeds, and (4) controlling insect pests. In most cases, only a whole package of new techniques can achieve such dramatic results.

A New Practice Must Promise Substantial Returns

A new technique must promise quite substantial increases in yield, or reduction in costs, to be acceptable to most farmers. A new strain of seed combined with a recommended application of fertilizer that is found on experimental plots to increase yields by 10 or 15 percent will be adopted by farmers only slowly, if at all. Different qualified experts have estimated the increased yield necessary to appeal to farmers in the beginning at different amounts, ranging from 40 to 100 percent.

The chief reason for this is that there is uncertainty as to how effective the new technique will be on each farmer's own fields. He is sure of what his past practices have yielded; he is not sure about the new. He knows how to apply established methods; he may not be confident of his ability to handle the new. In addition, he knows that poor weather may hold his crop far below the maximum obtainable in a good year.

Moreover, while new techniques need to be closely adjusted to soil and climatic factors, research stations cannot develop a different strain of a crop for each field. The best they can do is to develop combinations of practices that work reasonably well over a certain range of soil and climatic conditions. Consequently, each farmer rightly takes into account the possibility that the new techniques will not yield as much on his own fields as they do on the experimental plots of the nearest research station.

Only the promise of quite large additional returns can overcome the wise conservatism of farmers in the light of these risks and uncertainties.

Sources of New Technology

"New" here means new to a particular farmer. The method or the material may be common practice among certain other farmers either nearby or far away. It may be a modification of a similar practice or it may be an original discovery.

Practices of other farmers. It is seldom that all farmers in a region follow exactly the same practices and use exactly the same materials. Some practices and materials are more productive than others under local conditions. Consequently, one of the sources of new technology for an individual farmer can be the methods and materials used by other farmers nearby. Sometimes the superiority is so obvious that the farmer recognizes it easily and adopts the new technique at once. In other cases, a farmer may assume that the better results obtained by a neighbor are due not to the methods or materials used but to the skill of the neighbor or the greater fertility of his soil. Or, lacking careful measurement, farmers may not even know whether, or by how much, their harvests differ.

These differences among farmers in the methods they follow and the materials they use can be a valuable source of new technology for any farmer in the region who is not already employing the best methods.

At the same time there is a limit to how far such adoption of the best methods already in use in a region can carry agricultural development. Most agricultural regions are capable of far higher production than could be achieved through using the present practices of the best farmers. To come closer to achieving the maximum production of which a region is capable, additional sources of new technology must be sought.

Introduction from other regions. A second source of new technology is the methods and materials that have been developed in other regions or countries having similar agricultural characteristics. The variety of maize introduced into West Java in the example given on page 78 came originally from Guatemala. It was imported and tested in a research program in Indonesia. It will soon be replaced by a new variety from Latin America which has been further developed in a research program in southern India.

Most of the technology available to farmers in a rapidly developing agriculture has come from some other place. Maize has spread widely over the earth from its first cultivation in the American tropics.

79

Rubber was first tapped from forest trees in Brazil and spread from there to Malaya, Indonesia, Vietnam, and other countries. Fifty years ago, the United States imported Russian varieties of wheat to find strains better adapted to some of its needs. Introducing Japanese methods of rice culture has raised production in many other countries.

Techniques introduced from another region or country must always be carefully tested locally before being recommended to farmers. They may require modification to make them useful and acceptable locally.

Purposeful experimentation. The third source of new technology is experimental search for really new strains of crops, soil treatments, disease control measures, livestock medicines, machines, etc. Most of our modern insecticides, hybrid seeds, vitamin-enriched feeds and similar farm supplies have come from this source.

Just as the best methods now used by the best farmers in a region are not good enough for tomorrow, so the best technology that can be introduced from some other part of the world is not sufficient to assure a constantly improving agriculture. We must continually be developing really novel farm technology in order to keep agriculture moving ahead.

Research

The best definition of research, for our purpose in thinking about changing farm technology, is the most general one given by Webster's International Dictionary: *research is careful and diligent search.*

Within this definition, the careful and diligent search for the most productive methods now used by individual farmers in a region is research. The careful search for techniques, materials and practices from other regions or countries, and testing them for their usefulness locally, and perhaps modifying them, is also research. And research includes, as well, purposeful experimentation to develop really "new" materials and practices that can make agriculture more productive.

Many people prefer to reserve the word "research" for only the last of these three, and some would limit it further to only certain types of experimentation. The danger in this is that the other two important sources of new farm technology are likely to be slighted or neglected entirely. Moreover, the best and most productive purposeful experimentation frequently includes all three functions.

When the Ministry of Agriculture, aided by Rockefeller Foundation scientists, undertook to increase the production of maize in Mexico, their first step was to collect thousands of samples of maize varieties currently being grown in the country and to test these carefully against each other in field plots. From this alone they found a few that were clearly superior. In some cases they found that a strain being grown in one part of the country was better adapted to a different region and would increase local production when introduced there.

They next collected samples of varieties being grown in other countries and tested these under Mexican conditions in different parts of the country. The more complicated experimentation came later: the development of hybrid varieties, experimentation on fertilization, plant protection measures, and cultivation practices.

Governmental Experiment Stations

No country has achieved substantial agricultural development with-

A governmental research station in Colombia assisted by the Rockefeller Foundation agricultural program.

81

out establishing and maintaining efficient governmental experiment stations for agricultural research. Some farmers experiment with new crops and new cultural practices on their own farms. In more highly developed economies research is frequently carried on by commercial firms interested in selling seeds, fertilizers, implements and other supplies and equipment to farmers. These are helpful but they are not an adequate substitute for governmental agricultural research.

Whether a new program of governmental research is being established or an older one is being reorganized, there are two questions to be raised. First, are the individual projects of the research program well-suited to the country's needs? Second, is the research program organized in an effective manner and located in the right place or places?

Are the Right Problems Being Studied?

A high proportion of the projects should be such that they can quickly result in new techniques ready for farmers to use. Farmers need these results and the country needs the increased production that can flow from them.

The question of how much effort to put into the study of immediate problems and how much to devote to long-term, more "basic" research is not a problem for newly-established research programs alone; it persists as long as research is continued. The danger of not having enough study of immediate farm problems is usually greater than the danger of not having enough basic research.

Research workers frequently feel that doing basic research leads to higher professional standing than does engaging in "applied research." Yet it is important that the proportion of projects devoted to immediate problems of farmers be kept high, partly because farmers are in urgent need of their solution, and partly to insure that the research organization itself may continue to get adequate financial support. Legislators and the general public are more impressed by practical results already achieved than they are by the uncertain promise of large gains to be had sometime in the indefinite future from long-term and perhaps more basic research.

Also, it is advisable to concentrate research primarily on crops for which there is, or could be, a substantial market.

It is quite clear from the past record of agricultural development in different parts of the world that farmers accept innovations in the production of cash crops much more readily than in the production of crops grown for home consumption. The reason for this seems obvious. Innovations almost always require the purchase of supplies or equipment: seeds, fertilizers, pesticides, etc. Farmers are more willing to spend money for these if they are to be used in producing a crop that brings in money. To argue that it is equally important to increase the production of crops for home consumption, perhaps in order that more of the land of the farm can be devoted to cash crops, seems logical to the outsider, but it is not as persuasive to the farmer. He is more inclined to make cash outlays that will bring him more cash in return.

But "cash crops" does not mean only export crops, although it includes them. Too many countries are restricting the attention of large numbers of their best agricultural scientists to one or a few export crops. Equal attention needs to be given to cash crops for the domestic market, including crops only part of which are sold, with part being consumed by the farm family. It is a sad commentary on the use of research resources that in very few places has anything like adequate attention been given to developing new techniques for mixed farming primarily for domestic markets.

Is the Research Program Well Located, Organized, and Administered?

Location. An effective research program must combine two activities, each strategically located in the country: (1) one or more comprehensive experiment stations, each located where soils and climate are representative of an agricultural region of high potential; and (2) many testing stations or field trials scattered through many farming localities.

Each major experiment station needs to be located in a place having approximately the same soil and climatic resources as large areas of the good agricultural land of the country with access to markets and to farm equipment and supplies. Too frequently, such a central research station is located near the capital city for ease of administration by someone from the Ministry of Agriculture. This is convenient but it is a mistake unless natural conditions at that place are representative of large areas of the country's good agricultural land.

In addition to a central experiment station, it is important to carry on local adaptive research at a number of widely scattered points, preferably in close coordination with the extension program. This local adaptive research can in some cases be carried out on fields of individual farmers if it is given close supervision. In other cases small research farms can be established. These need not have much in the way of laboratory facilities. They do need adequate equipment for field operations of the same type being recommended to farmers, and they need facilities for the careful measuring and recording of research results in the field. Their function is to carry on such experimentation as (1) comparative yield tests of seed carefully selected from the best farmers' fields as well as of seeds developed at the experiment stations, (2) experimental plantings of seeds from other regions, and (3) fertilizer trials at different levels of fertilization and including information on costs and returns.

Organization. The organization of an experiment station needs two special qualities in addition to the normal requirements of good organization. First, it should be such that research specialists of different technical fields are able and encouraged to cooperate on individual projects. Second, it should assure that each new technique being developed or tested is assessed from the standpoint of its effect on the whole farm business.

Few farm problems can be satisfactorily solved by research scientists of a single specialty. If the central problem is to breed plants for higher yields, the question of the most profitable rate of fertilizing the new strain invariably arises, as does that of how the value of the increased yield compares with the cost of achieving it. If the problem is one of how to protect plants from pests or diseases, it always involves the engineering problem of how the control measure can be applied, as well as the comparison of costs and returns. For such reasons each research staff needs to include scientists of several different specialties.

In addition to having scientists of different specialties on the staff, it is important to have a number of individual projects set up in such a way that the various specialists have to work together. Some experiment stations already do this effectively. The whole staff of each station participates in selecting projects of high priority to their region after constant close contact with extension agents and farmers. They then organize each project so that all of the relevant specialists have a role in it and carry it through together.

Furthermore, the more varied the specialized interests of different members of a research staff the more they may stimulate each other and the greater is the likelihood that all relevant factors will be taken into account in tackling each problem. Large numbers of research workers alone will not accomplish this. Competence, imagination, and wise leadership are required also. Given these, however, there is a minimum size of an effective research organization below which the work of the staff will not be fully effective.

Each experiment station needs to be so organized that it takes adequate account of the impact of each new technique on the farm business as a whole. Too frequently, research results are recommended to farmers without the cash costs and returns having been calculated, or without the impact of the proposed new technique on the whole farm business having been taken into account. To achieve this over-all consideration of the effect of a new technique requires day-to-day cooperation of research specialists from different fields, including the agricultural economist as well as physical and biological scientists. It also requires close cooperation with farmers and extension workers.

Too frequently, also, research stations are set up to deal with only one crop. This may be justifiable in the case of a plantation crop normally grown to the exclusion of all others on individual farms. Even here, however, there is an advantage in having the station experiment with other crops that might be introduced on the same farms. In general, it is usually better not to have separate research facilities for individual crops but to have the responsibility of each station cover all of the major crops of the region. This need not preclude concentration of major research effort on selected crops for a particular period of time.

Administration. First, experiment stations must have adequate financial support. Adequate salaries for a sufficient number of scientists to work effectively together must be accompanied by adequate pro-

85

vision for research equipment and operating expenses for research projects. Agricultural research can be highly profitable to a country. But this high return cannot be achieved without making the investment. There is no point in starting agricultural research stations at all unless they can be adequately financed, giving their scientists good working equipment, adequate budgets and attractive salaries.

The next most important requirement for effective administration of agricultural research is qualified and competent leadership. Such leadership includes the ability to combine: (1) a reasonable amount of freedom for individual staff members, and (2) focus on high priority problems, with (3) mutual professional stimulation between staff scientists of varied specialties and with frequent contact with farmers and extension workers.

Workers in other activities related to agriculture are frequently reluctant to approach research workers, perhaps because research workers are often more highly trained and seem to "speak a different

". . . it is important that there be a training component in practically every research project at early stages of agricultural development."

language." But research workers need the pressure of farmers and of workers in other agricultural fields in order to help them select really high priority topics for investigation. And farmers and extension workers need to know what research is being carried on.

Good Questions for Assessing
a Research Program

1. Is the emphasis of the research program on products for which there is a market?

2. Do a high proportion of the individual research projects seek answers to immediate farm problems?

3. Is there at least one comprehensive research station located in a region of high agricultural potential?

4. What adaptive research is being carried on at a number of widely scattered points in cooperation with extension?

5. Do specialists from different fields cooperate in the same projects?

6. Is the economic impact of each recommended practice on total farm businesses studied as part of the research?

7. Are salaries for research workers adequate to attract competent men?

8. Does the research budget provide for adequate working equipment?

9. Is training in research methods associated with most research projects?

Research and Training

Every country needs more well-trained research workers. Participation in research projects is an essential part of the training of such workers. For this reason it is important that there be a training component in practically every research project at early stages of agricultural development. This is made easier where research is conducted by colleges or universities that are also engaged in resident instruction of students. It can be achieved, however, even in research organizations that are separate from universities, if they establish research apprenticeships or internships that train young men in elementary research procedures.

The Rockefeller Foundation Agricultural Program in Mexico is a good example of a program devoted simultaneously to getting research results and to training research workers.

Other ways to accomplish this are exemplified by the Community Development Research Council of the University of the Philippines, and the Indian Council of Agricultural Research. In both India and the Philippines most agricultural research is carried on by special governmental agencies. But a professor in a college of agriculture or in a university can apply to one of these central research organizations for financial support for a specific research project. He can then carry this on in connection with his training of college and university students, both getting some needed research done and improving the preparation of potential research workers.

———————

Farm technology must keep changing if agricultural productivity is to continue to increase. Well directed and competent research is the chief means to this end. For the most part, such research needs to be devoted to crops for which there is an established market that gives promise of absorbing increased production without too great a drop in price. (This is an example of the fact that the "essentials" of agricultural development are not independent; they affect each other and each must be considered in the light of the others.)

CHAPTER 7

Local Availability
of Supplies and Equipment

Most of the new methods that will increase agricultural production require the use by farmers of special supplies or equipment. These include seeds, fertilizers, pesticides, livestock feeds and medicines, and tools. Agricultural development requires that these be available at many, many local points in sufficient quantity to meet the needs of every farmer who may want to use them.

Manufacture or Importation

Most farm supplies and equipment have to be manufactured.

Fertilizers are sometimes made simply by crushing suitable mineral materials, but usually by chemical processes. The minerals required are found only in certain places, so the fertilizers made from them frequently have to be imported.

The fertilizers that are made by chemical processes usually require large manufacturing plants if they are to be produced cheaply enough to be sold at reasonable prices. The amount of such fertilizers that farmers are ready to buy may or may not be great enough to make it economic to set up one or more manufacturing plants within the country. If it is not, that fertilizer will have to be imported, at least for the present.

Most pesticides and livestock medicines are chemical compounds. Like fertilizers, these must either be manufactured or imported.

While much of the feed for livestock may come from forage crops and grains grown on the farm where they are fed, some of the feeds needed for progressive livestock management have to be specially

89

prepared. It is possible for farmers to mix some of these themselves but it is more efficient in many cases for such feeds to be manufactured. Many livestock feeds are made largely from materials like bran, oil cake, rice hulls, molasses, and mash from fermented grains that are by-products of industries processing human foods.

Only the simplest tools and implements can be made locally and by hand. Some can be manufactured in small plants using power machinery. Others are more efficiently produced by large-scale methods.

The great need of agricultural development for manufactured supplies and equipment suggests that this kind of manufacturing should be given high priority in each country's plans for industrialization. Sometimes it will prove to be more economical to import a particular input than to manufacture it, but each case should be carefully studied.

Multiplication of Seeds

Once a new strain of a crop plant has been developed by research, the seeds of it must be multiplied until there is enough to meet the demand of the farmers who want to purchase it.

One way is to establish seed multiplication farms operated by the government. This is usually the most expensive method. If it is done on very large seed multiplication farms, each serving a wide area, the cost of transporting the seed to distant farmers is high. If seed is grown on a large number of government seed multiplication farms widely dispersed over the country, the program requires a large number of trained technicians and a complicated administration.

A second technique for seed multiplication is to establish a system of "certified growers." These are farmers who develop a special business of multiplying seed for use by other farmers. This method decreases the operating administrative problems involved in government seed multiplication farms. However, it requires a regulatory organization to insure that the quality and purity of the seed is maintained. This method has been used quite effectively in recent years in Taiwan.

A third arrangement for seed multiplication is to provide a small amount of improved seed to one or a few of the farmers in each lo-

90

In Mexico, the Maize Commission, multiplies improved seed, treats it for disease control,

. . . stores it

. . . and distributes it.

91

cality for them to multiply for use by other farmers in the vicinity. This method brings transportation costs down to a minimum. It also reduces the problem of maintaining purity of the seed since the multiplication of the seed is carried on under the eyes of the farmers who are planning to use it. Farmers see the process and can observe how the seed is handled. In addition, seeing the improved variety growing locally stimulates farmers to try it themselves.

Each of these three methods can work.

Salability of Supplies and Equipment

What supplies and equipment will farmers actually buy and use? Each item of supplies or equipment must have five qualities if farmers are to buy it and keep on buying it year after year:

1. It must be technically effective.
2. It must be of dependable quality.
3. The price of it must be reasonable.
4. It must be available locally precisely when farmers need to use it.
5. It must be offered for sale in appropriate sizes or amounts.

Technical effectiveness. The first quality a seed, fertilizer, or other item must possess in order to be salable is technical effectiveness. Is the "improved" seed really better? Too frequently, recommendations are based only on the yield per acre at a research station. Unless the seed has been tested locally, however, local soils and climates may be sufficiently different that the improved seed yields no better than strains already in common use. Or if the yield is higher but the growing period is different, using this new variety may interfere with the cultivation of other crops or it may expose the farmer's crop to unusual damage by birds because his crop ripens at a different time from that of his neighbors. Or the taste or cooking quality of a new variety may be sufficiently different to make it unpopular.

Does the livestock medicine really work? Does the implement do the job it is supposed to do? Is it better than the one the farmer has now?

This question of technical effectiveness is the first one on which a farmer must be satisfied before he will buy a new input. If he buys it once he certainly will not buy it again unless it really works.

92

Farmers need to be able to buy their supplies and equipment locally and in convenient quantities like the Mexican poultry farmers (left) who buy one bag of feed at a time and carry it home. For the Syrian farmer (right) the correct kind of dust and a one man duster are essential to his being able to protect his cotton from insects.

Quality dependability. Unfortunately, an improved seed, a pure pesticide, or a fertilizer of precise chemical composition cannot be identified by sight, smell, taste or touch. Even inferior quality of tools or implements is often not easy to detect in the market place. For this reason a prime requirement for widespread and repeated purchase of a new input is sufficiently careful control of quality that farm operators develop confidence in their sources of supply.

Entirely too frequently what is sold as "improved seed" turns out to be ordinary grain. Or livestock feeds are adulterated with nearly useless "fillers." Or something is sold as "fertilizer" without the farmer being able to tell just what is in it.

There is no easy solution to this problem. Regulations requiring that each package of fertilizer, pesticide, and livestock feed carry a label precisely describing its contents can help if these are followed up by inspections and stiff penalties for misrepresentation.

Farmers are not fools. They will buy only what they think will work. They will not *continue* to buy if they are cheated or misled as to the quality of the supplies and equipment offered to them. They must have confidence in those from whom they buy and they have confidence only in those who prove themselves honest, whether the merchant is a private person or a government agency or a cooperative society.

Price relationships. How much does it cost, considering what it will do? It is not maximum physical production that the farmer seeks. What he wants is a substantial margin between the costs of the various inputs he uses and the market value of his products. He will not buy a fertilizer or another input just because its price is low if it is not technically effective or if the quality is uncertain. He will pay a reasonable price if it does meet those tests. Either way he takes account of price, especially the *relationship* between prices of inputs and the prices he can get for his products.

Quite frequently a substantial part of the price a farmer pays for one of these inputs is the cost of transporting it from the manufacturing plant, seed farm, or seaport to the local market. Consequently, local price relationships between inputs and outputs will be different for farms at different locations.

This is illustrated by the drawing on the following page. At Point A a bag of fertilizer that costs $3 will increase a wheat harvest by 5 bushels. The wheat can be sold there for $1 per bushel, or a total of $5. This gives the farmer a margin of $2 for each bag of fertilizer he uses.

At Point B the same bag of fertilizer costs $3.25 because of the cost of trucking it from the railway. A farmer at Point B can get only $0.90 per bushel for his wheat, or a total of $4.50 for the 5 bushels, because of the costs of trucking it back to the railway. This leaves him a margin of only $1.25 (instead of the $2 gained by the farmer at Point A).

At Point C, located some distance away from the highway, the bag of fertilizer costs $3.75 and a farmer there gets only $0.70 per bushel for his wheat, or a total of $3.50 for the 5 additional bushels of wheat that the fertilizer makes possible. This leaves him with a net loss of $0.25, even though the technical effectiveness of the fertilizer is the same at Point C as at Point A.

Transportation costs make local price relationships between inputs and outputs different for farms at different locations—see text.

These price relationships are an important part of the salability of any input.

Availability when needed. The need for each input is highly seasonal. Seeds must be available shortly before planting time and can seldom be sold at any other time of the year. Fertilizers must be applied at specific times and few farmers have facilities for storing them satisfactorily. The same is true of pesticides, although small amounts of them can be held for future use.

This means that those who offer supplies and equipment for sale must be intimately acquainted with the seasonality of the need for each separate input and foresighted in having adequate supplies of

95

each on hand ahead of time so that farmers may get them quickly when they are needed.

Size of container. The size of the containers in which many supplies are offered for sale is also important. Too frequently containers hold more than a small farm needs at any one time and farmers may not have facilities for storing the extra amount until the following year when it may be needed again.

Local Testing

Most farmers are reluctant to try a new input when it first becomes available. Most adults, anywhere, want to be confident of good results before they will try something new in the presence of their neighbors.

Unless the material is tested in many localities, under conditions practically identical with those on a farmer's land, the farmer can be justifiably skeptical as to whether it will work for him on his own farm or will be profitable even if it does work.

Consequently, local testing almost becomes another essential in the salability of supplies and equipment.

"Packages" of Inputs

It was noted in Chapter 1 and again in Chapter 6 that each change in farming methods usually requires other changes. This has led to the popularity, in recent years, of the idea of "package programs" in which several new inputs are introduced at the same time. To make package programs possible, local arrangements for the distribution of farm supplies and equipment need to be such that all of the inputs that can reinforce each other are available in the same local markets.

Uncertain Demand by Farmers

There is no way to foresee accurately how long it will be after a new input becomes available in a local market before a large number of farmers begin to buy it. Most farm operators wait until someone else has tried it first on a nearby farm. Only after the use of the input has been justified by local testing and by independent use by neighboring farmers, and a climate of opinion has developed that "this is good and worth what it costs," will many farmers begin to use it in quantity.

Consequently, to spur agricultural development, particularly at early stages, supplies of inputs locally available should be larger than the probable early demand for them so that no willing innovator may have to forego trying them. Because of this, distributors may need credit to encourage them to stock supplies greater than the proved demand, and they may need arrangements for taking unsold stocks off their hands when the season has passed.

In Peru, a phased pattern of distribution of supplies and equipment was introduced about 1950. In this system, seeds, fertilizers, pesticides and implements were made available through a central governmental agency and by private suppliers to those private merchants who wished to stock them locally. Meanwhile, modest stocks of each were kept on hand at the local offices of the governmental extension service, and these stocks were replenished as needed from a central

"Many livestock feeds are by-products of industries processing human foods." Pineapple pulp being fed to beef cattle in the Philippines.

supply depot. The price at which each input was offered at the extension office was slightly higher than that at which a private merchant in the same locality would have to sell it in order to cover his costs and an acceptable margin. The result of this system was that when a new input was first recommended for local use, farm operators could get it through the extension office. As demand increased, local private merchants began offering it at a slightly lower price and the task of distributing that particular input gradually shifted from governmental into private channels. The government continued to stock the items in extension offices, primarily as a check on the prices charged by private merchants.

In this way private merchants did not have to stock the new input until after they were sure farmers would be willing to buy it in considerable quantities. At the same time, the government extension offices only had to *pioneer* in offering inputs for sale. Once an effective demand had developed, private merchants relieved them of this task and the extension service had only to keep small amounts on hand as a check on prices and quality.

The problems discussed in this chapter should make it clear that putting adequate amounts of farm supplies and equipment where farmers can buy them is complex and difficult to achieve. Whatever the difficulties, it *must be accomplished* if agricultural productivity is to rise. If it is to be accomplished, it must receive as much and as competent attention as research or the arrangements for marketing farm products.

CHAPTER 8

Production Incentives for Farmers

Improved farm practices, access to markets for farm products and the availability of supplies and equipment—these provide opportunities for farmers to increase production, but will they use them?

Here we must go back to the nature of the farmer. He is a *person* managing a *business*. As a person he wants his family to be well cared for and he wants a respected place for himself and his family in the community. Being a farmer, he must seek to reach these goals through his farming.

At early stages of the commercialization of agriculture he is interested first in seeing that his family has enough to eat, and wants to guarantee this by producing it at home. To meet the other needs of his family, he wants to sell enough products that he can pay his taxes or his rent, meet payments on his debts, if any, and buy necessities that he cannot produce for the family. As additional goods and services become available in his locality he wants to obtain some of these for his family: education for his children, medical services, and articles such as bicycles, better clothing, radios, better household furnishings and special kinds of food.

To accomplish these aims through his farm business he must pay close attention to costs and returns. He must sell products worth more in the market than it costs him to produce them. The margin between costs and returns, the farmer's *net income,* must keep increasing if he is to be able to give his family a rising level of living.

Thus, the incentives that can be effective in getting farmers to increase their production are primarily economic:

1. remunerative price relationships
2. a reasonable share of the harvest
3. the availability of goods and services that farmers would like to be able to purchase for themselves and their families.

All of these, together in combination, provide the strongest economic incentives to farmers.

There are other incentives besides economic ones. Farmers want respect and recognition from their friends and neighbors. We shall come back to this at the end of the chapter. But the most important incentives are economic and we shall discuss them first.

Remunerative Price Relationships

To the extent that a farmer produces for the market, his incentive to increase production depends on the relationship between the price he will receive for his product and the costs of producing it. These costs of production are influenced by the prices he must pay for purchased inputs.

Prices for farm products. Both the *level* and the *dependability* of prices for farm products influence the degree to which they provide incentives to farmers to increase production.

When other essentials for agricultural development are available, the higher the price offered to farmers for a particular farm product, the more of it they will produce and bring to the market. Many people do not believe this, and government policies often are based on the assumption that it is not so. Where evidence is cited to prove that prices do not matter, it is almost always found, on examination, that the reason lies in the fact that one or another of the *other* essentials for agricultural development has not been met. A remunerative price for farm products is not the only essential for development but it is an important one.

A recent series of studies in the State of Punjab in India revealed that farmers there shift from producing one crop to producing another in response to price changes to at least the same degree as do the highly commercial farmers of the United States.

Similarly, there is increasing evidence that farmers seek to *increase the production per acre of a particular crop* when the price of that

Both the level and the dependability of prices are important to farmers like the Burmese rice grower above receiving payment from the marketing board depot manager.

crop rises, particularly by purchasing increasing amounts of fertilizer for use on the crop. In Indonesia, where prices of farm products had been held down, controls were abandoned in 1964 and prices allowed to seek their own level. Farm prices shot up. Farmers became more interested in fertilizers and improved seed. Land was farmed more intensively and larger amounts of rice, corn, vegetables, and other cash crops came on the market.

Farmers *do* respond to market prices, and if a country wants agricultural development the prices offered to individual farmers must be favorable.

The *dependability* of prices for farm products is as important as their level.

Most agricultural product prices fluctuate widely within each year, with prices usually lowest just after harvest time. Most farmers do not have facilities for storing their crops without losses due to insects

101

or spoilage. Also, they are usually short of cash and need to sell as soon as they can. Hence, many farm operators feel compelled to sell their products immediately after harvest and this is one reason why prices are lowest at that time.

Prices of farm products fluctuate also from year to year, depending on how big the harvest may have been in the previous year, on what carry-over stocks are on hand, and on the prospects for the harvest in the current year.

Unfortunately, fluctuations in agricultural product prices are likely to be particularly great just at that stage in agricultural development when farmers need to begin to sell more and more of the products of their farms.

Where most of the population is still on farms, so that the domestic off-farm demand for farm products is still relatively small, modest increases in production can have large effects in pushing market prices down. Furthermore, marketing facilities needed for transporting, storing, processing, and other handling of the increased supplies usually are slow in developing. This tends particularly to depress prices in local markets at harvest time.

Previously farmers have produced primarily for home consumption. Now, just when they must rely on market prices of their products in calculating costs and returns, they are faced not by stable and predictable prices but by great uncertainty.

Furthermore, this situation is frequently aggravated when governments place ceilings on agricultural product prices. The argument for setting maximum prices for farm products usually is the desire to hold down the cost of living of urban people—industrial workers and government employees. The result is to reduce the incentives to each farm operator to increase his production just when agricultural development is of prime importance to the nation.

Sometimes farmers increase their production of a crop in response to high prices only to abandon this crop later when they discover that its market price is not dependable. Farmers in Brazil shifted large acreages to sugarcane, but reverted to growing cereals due to the extreme instability of the price for sugar.

Influencing farm prices. Recognizing that the level and dependability of farm product prices are important to agricultural develop-

102

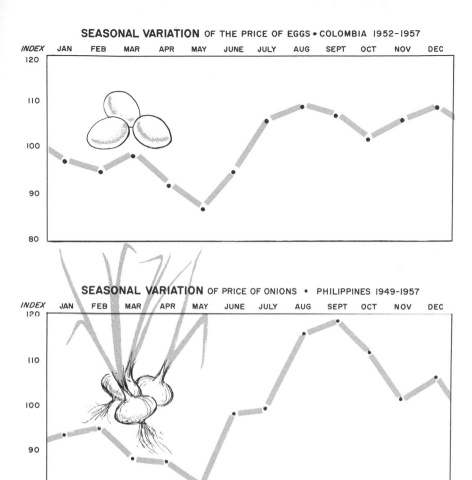

SEASONAL VARIATION OF THE PRICE OF EGGS • COLOMBIA 1952-1957

SEASONAL VARIATION OF PRICE OF ONIONS • PHILIPPINES 1949-1957

"Most agricultural product prices fluctuate widely within each year."

ment is one thing; doing something about them poses complex problems that are not easy to solve.

No program to affect farm product prices can be effective in the absence of efficient marketing facilities.

If marketing facilities are inadequate or inefficient, steps should be taken to improve them. If there is monopoly in the market, this may need to be regulated, or encouragement may be given to cooperatives or other new marketing firms to provide competition. Or a government agency may undertake to buy and sell a commodity at reasonable prices, thus providing an alternative marketing channel. To

103

undertake this, however, the agency must have access to the physical facilities needed to handle the commodities it buys. Otherwise it will not be able to make good its guarantees, and the result will be worse than if no regulation of prices had been attempted.

Direct regulation of prices for farm products can be of value, but only if wisely and effectively done, and considerable administrative efforts are always involved. It is important to recognize that prices cannot be regulated merely by passing a law. Complicated programs of inspection, and usually of government purchase, storage, and sale of those commodities for which prices are regulated are necessary. In view of the complications, it is best to limit price regulation to only those few commodities of which increased production is most needed. And for these commodities, the first aim should be to increase the *certainty* of prices, at levels that will be remunerative to efficient producers.

If it is felt necessary to hold down the cost of food to urban consumers, it is better to do this by government subsidy within the food distribution process than it is to choke off the source of supply by setting low product prices for farmers that deter them from adopting measures to increase production.

Farmers will not grow more just because the nation needs greater

THAILAND   INDIA   JAPAN

The relation of farm product prices to the cost of supplies is an important aspect of incentives. The Thai farmer has to produce five times as much rice to pay for one bag of fertilizer as the Japanese farmer and the Indian farmer three times as much. It is not surprising, therefore, that Japanese farmers use much more fertilizer than those in Thailand or India.

104

agricultural production. They will only do this, they *can* only do it, to the extent that it is profitable for them to do so, and one of the factors affecting this profitability is the level and the dependability of the prices of farm products.

Prices for supplies and equipment. Prices for farm products comprise one-half of "remunerative price relationships"; the other half is prices for the inputs a farmer may purchase.

An example of how the relationship between the prices of rice and fertilizer differs among countries is indicated in the following table. These figures show that whereas it takes only about one kilogram of rice to buy one kilogram of either nitrogenous or phosphatic fertilizer in Pakistan or Japan, in India it requires three to four times as much.

Quantity of Rice (in kilograms) Required
To Purchase One Kilogram of Fertilizer.[1]

Country	(1962) Ammonium Sulphate	Super Phosphate (more than 25% P_2O_5)
Pakistan	0.85	0.89
Japan	1.18	1.00
U.S.A.	1.47	1.02
India	3.82	3.19

[1] Calculated from data from FAO *Production Yearbook,* vol. 17, 1963 by Department of Agricultural Economics, University of Minnesota.

Clearly there is more price incentive for a farmer to use fertilizer in rice production in Pakistan or Japan than there is in India as long as these price relationships hold. But here again we must remind ourselves that it is the relationship between the cost of inputs and *the amount by which they will increase production* that is important.

Like the prices of farm products, the prices of inputs are often substantially influenced by governmental policies. On the one hand, governments frequently impose heavy import duties on farm supplies and equipment to stimulate domestic manufacture of them. Such a policy penalizes farmers from the beginning, and may give rise to domestic industries that can exist only with such protection for a long time to come. To stimulate such domestic manufacture is frequently a sound policy, but to do it in such a way that farmers are discouraged from adopting more productive methods is self-defeating for the total economy of the country.

On the other hand, many governments subsidize the cost of certain inputs to farmers in order to stimulate their use. This does stimulate agricultural development, but whether or not it is the best policy to pursue depends on a number of considerations that vary from country to country.

To repeat, what is of greatest importance is the *relationship* between prices of farm products and prices of purchasable inputs. This relationship can be affected by allowing prices of both agricultural products and of purchasable inputs to be left free of specific controls or subsidies, or by placing controls or subsidies on either, or on both. Each of these has its advantages and disadvantages. It is possible to use them in different combinations. What is important is not so much the particular combination of policies chosen as recognition that the relationship between prices for farm products and for farm inputs is of major importance to the strength of the incentives for farmers to increase production.

The effect of the prices of farm products and of farm inputs on the incentives of farmers to increase production may be summarized as follows:

1. Farmers will increase their production for the market only when they consider the price offered for a particular farm product in the local market to be attractive.

2. Farmers will respond to changes in the relative prices of crops they are already growing by increasing production of the crop offering the greater value in the market, unless they feel that this will jeopardize the food supply of the farm family.

3. Farmers will respond to an increase in price of a particular crop by using improved methods to increase their production of it (1) if the necessary inputs are locally available, (2) if the farmer feels he knows how to use these inputs

106

effectively, and (3) if the price of these inputs is not too high in comparison with the promised value of the product.

4. Improving the efficiency of marketing to reduce the costs of handling, shipping, and processing farm products can increase the local prices received by farmers for their products, or decrease the price to the ultimate consumer, or both.

Share of the Harvest

The farmer who is a share tenant does not consider as income the share of the harvest that goes to the landlord. If he is considering the use of new techniques that promise to raise production he takes into account only the value of that share of the harvest that will be his. If he has to pay the full additional cost of the new techniques, his incentive to adopt new techniques is much weaker than if he is either an owner-operator or a cash tenant, with the cash rent remaining the same regardless of level of production.

This is illustrated on the following page. The illustration assumes that the purchase of $1 of additional inputs will yield an additional product worth $3. If the farmer owns the farm or is a cash tenant, he can count on a *net* addition to his income of $2 for each $1 spent on the new method. If he is a share tenant, however, this additional net income shrinks to $0.50 for each $1 spent on the new techniques.

This influence of the share of the harvest on the incentives of farmers to increase production is one reason for encouraging the ownership of farms by their operators. Replacing share rentals by cash rentals can have the same beneficial effect on incentives, provided the landlord does not raise the cash rent as productivity increases. Even with share rentals, the incentive to farm operators can be altered by reducing the share of the crop going to the landlord.

Another approach, where share tenancy is retained, is to divide the costs of new techniques between landlord and tenant in the same proportion as the harvest is divided. This is done effectively in a number of places. The difficulty in it is that it divides the decision-making between the landlord and the tenant. If one is less eager for development than the other, the conflict between them slows down the adoption of new practices.

TYPE OF FARMER	DISTRIBUTION OF HARVEST				CALCULATION OF INCENTIVE	
	OLD METHOD		NEW METHOD		INCREASE	INCENTIVE TO FARMER
	FARMER'S SHARE	LANDLORD'S SHARE	FARMER'S SHARE	LANDLORD'S SHARE	$\dfrac{VALUE}{\text{FARMER'S SHARE}}$ $\dfrac{COST}{\text{NEW METHOD}}$	
OWNER-OPERATOR					$3.00 $1.00	$2.00
SHARE-TENANT					$1.50 $1.00	$ .50
CASH-TENANT					$3.00 $1.00	$2.00

The share tenant's incentive to adopt new methods is much weaker than the owner operator's or the cash tenant's.

Availability of Goods and Services Farm Families Would Like to Have

If goods and services that farm families would like to have are on sale nearby, this provides an additional incentive to farmers to produce for the market: the more things they want to buy, the more farm products they must sell in order to get the money to pay for these goods and services.

Making goods and services available to farm people presents a problem of market development similar to that of developing the domestic market for farm products. Marketing channels for distributing industrial products in rural areas are likely to be inadequate and inefficient. Those manufacturing such products, or who might do so, are likely to think chiefly of selling to urban consumers who are near at hand and readily reached through existing marketing channels.

Nevertheless, as has been previously pointed out, in most developing countries farm people are a large potential market for consumer

108

goods as well as for agricultural production inputs, and development of this market is important for industrial development. That making goods and services available to farm families is also a spur to agricultural development illustrates again the interdependence of agriculture and industry in overall economic development. Special attention should therefore be given to stimulating the production and distribution of attractive consumer goods for farm families.

Home Education for Women

The desire of farm families to purchase goods and services to raise their level of living is stimulated by seeing these locally available. In many cases, however, rural people do not know how some of these can be used effectively. In addition, the same fear of ridicule or disapproval operates on women as on men in traditional rural societies. Educational programs for rural women help them learn better ways of caring for their families and encourage changes in ways of living. As these changes become known and desirable to them, farm people want to increase the net incomes of their farms in order to be able to afford more purchases for use by the farm family.

Japan has over 1500 women working full-time as extension agents to rural women in its Home Life Improvement Program, administered by the Ministry of Agriculture. In Brazil, the Association for Rural Credit and Assistance has one woman extension agent working with each agricultural agent. In that program, planning for improvement of the home and of the life of the family is combined with planning for improvement of the farm business.

Some people think that a program for the improvement of rural homes and family living is a "frill," an expensive luxury that a country eager to achieve economic development cannot afford. It is doubtful that this is true, and for very good economic reasons. Instead, it is likely that raising the hopes of village families for a better life, and helping them learn how to achieve this, stimulates increased agricultural production. Learning to meet some of these needs by using materials and time already available to them without waiting for any government to act causes them to develop a more confident attitude toward life in general. Learning how to use goods and services that they can buy locally pushes them into increasing agricultural production for the market in order to have more money to spend on things for family use.

Public Recognition of Achievement

Another incentive to farmers to increase the production of their farms comes from public recognition for being successful farmers. If a nation proclaims as its heroes only soldiers, politicians and athletes, farmers conclude that these are the only pursuits the government feels are worthwhile. If it holds a celebration when a steel mill is completed but not when a farmer doubles his rice crop it seems as though industrialization is an achievement but becoming a modern farmer is not. In too many countries farmers receive little recognition. Yet farmers, like all human beings, want and need recognition. If raising agricultural production becomes a way to achieve public recognition, farmers have an added incentive to improve.

Public recognition is never a substitute for economic incentives, but it can help if it is in addition to these. The farmer must, first of all, stay in business and, if possible, prosper. For him to do this, remunerative price relationships and a reasonable share of the harvest are essential.

CHAPTER 9

Transportation

There is a fifth essential for agricultural development: transportation. Without transportation—efficient and low-cost—the other four essentials cannot be effectively provided.

The importance of transportation follows from what was pointed out in Chapter 1: that agricultural production must be widely dispersed. Farms must be spread out over the countryside to use the sunshine, the soil and other climatic conditions that will support crop growth wherever these are found. A correspondingly widespread transportation network is required to bring supplies and equipment to each farm, and to take products from farms to consumers in the towns and cities.

Furthermore, to provide favorable incentives to farmers transportation must be as inexpensive as possible. The cost to a farmer of an input like fertilizer is its price at the factory *plus* the cost of getting it from there to his farm. His return for the wheat or rice or other products he sells is the price in the central market *minus* the cost of getting the products from his farm to the market. As shown in Chapter 7, if transportation costs are too high, he will find fertilizer too expensive and the return for his wheat or rice too low. But if transportation costs can be brought down, the cost of the fertilizer *at his farm* will be lower and the return for his wheat or rice will be higher.

Looking back at the illustration on page 95, suppose that a road is built so that goods can be hauled direct from A to C by motor truck and that this cuts the cost of transportation between the two points in half. Suppose that this reduces the cost of a bag of fertilizer at C from $3.75 to $3.35 and increases the price of wheat at C from $0.70 to $0.85 per bushel. Since using a bag of fertilizer under the conditions of this illustration yields 5 additional bushels of wheat, the margin of returns over costs becomes $0.90 per bag of fertilizer. Building the road and reducing the hauling cost has provided the farmer at C an incentive to use the new input, whereas before it did not pay him to do so.

Factors Affecting Transportation Cost

The cost of transportation depends upon a number of factors. One is the nature of the commodity to be hauled—how heavy or bulky it is, whether it requires special packaging or careful handling to protect it from damage, whether it is perishable and must be moved quickly. Farm products vary widely in these respects—from grain, that can be shipped in bulk, to fresh fruits that are perishable and require special packaging, careful handling and rapid shipment to get them to their destinations before they spoil.

Three other factors upon which the cost of transportation depends are the distance the goods are shipped, the quantity that is shipped at one time, and the kind of conveyance that is used.

Differences in transportation costs make different crops advantageous even on farms of similar physical characteristics. The transportation that is available to a locality affects not only the *rate* of agricultural development there, it also affects the *kind* of agriculture —the particular crops and livestock products—that can economically be produced in the locality.

Local Transport

Agricultural transportation presents two kinds of situations with respect to distance, quantity, and type of conveyance. Farm products are brought to local market towns in small lots, from nearby farms or villages. At the local markets they are combined into larger lots for longer-distance shipment to central markets. Farm supplies and equipment go through the reverse process. They are shipped in large lots from factories or ports of entry to the market towns. There they are divided into small lots for local distribution to surrounding vil-

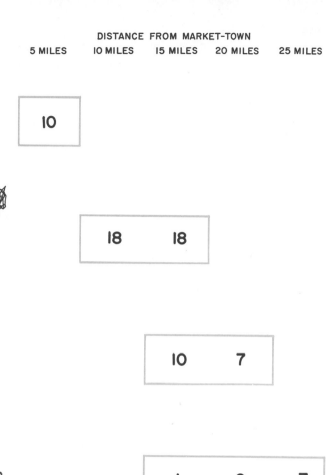

| | DISTANCE FROM MARKET-TOWN | | | | |
	5 MILES	10 MILES	15 MILES	20 MILES	25 MILES
Head Load	10				
Light Horse-Drawn Passenger Cart		18	18		
Bullock Cart			10	7	
Motor Transport			1	9	7
Sold at Farm			1	9	17	40

Number of farmers marketing and transporting grapes by different methods at increasing distances from the market-town.

lages and farms.

In early stages of development, farmers commonly provide much of the local transportation themselves. They carry products to market in head loads or on pack animals. Obviously, they cannot carry on a very extensive trade in this fashion. They market only a few things, in small quantities, and they buy little, depending on their own production for most of their subsistence.

The expansion of trade requires the building of roads over which carts or trucks can travel, carrying larger loads and over longer distances.

The mixed pattern of local transportation that may develop is well illustrated by a recent study of the marketing of fresh grapes in the vicinity of Bangalore, India. It was found that most growers within 5 miles of the market carried their grapes there by head load in bamboo baskets. Most of those 5 to 15 miles away used a light horse-drawn cart. Some, 10 to 20 miles away, used a larger cart drawn by bullocks. Most growers more than 15 miles away, if they took their own grapes to the market, made use of motor transport—buses, station wagons, or trucks. But at the greater distances, an increasing proportion did not take their grapes to market themselves but sold them on the vine to buyers who harvested and marketed them.

Building of local roads by farmers. Farmers themselves are capable of doing much of the work required for building or improving local roads. In the village of Tegalega, Indonesia, where a new package of practices increased maize production by 600%, village people improved a road to the highway so that the 35 tons of fertilizer and 200 tons of maize that had to be moved each year could move by truck.

In the Philippines a study was made of the savings in the cost of building rural roads under a self-help program. Land for the roads, locally available materials and most of the labor were contributed by local people. The national government provided engineering services and necessary heavy equipment. It also furnished special materials for bridges and culverts. The average cost per kilometer without "self-help" was ₱9,200; for the "self-help" roads it was ₱3,700. Obviously such a self-help system makes possible building many more roads with a given amount of government expenditure.

114

Effects of local roads in the Philippines. The Philippine study mentioned above also surveyed the changes affecting agriculture that followed the building of unpaved feeder roads connecting farming communities to a paved highway to which they had previously had no road access. A year after the roads were built, sales of corn and tobacco were about twice as great as before. Sales of chickens increased by two-thirds. For some products there was also a substantial increase in the price at the village relative to that in the central market. For corn, this increase was almost 25 percent. As a consequence, the average gross income of each village family from sales of the products studied increased from ₱492 per year to ₱785 per year.

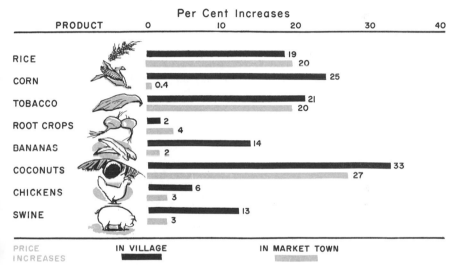

Comparative average increases in the prices of farm commodities a year after the opening of feeder roads.

In addition, these new roads brought into the locality many new influences bearing in one way or another on agricultural development. Visits to the locality by educational and service officials of the government increased dramatically (page 117). The greatest increase was in visits by social workers and medical personnel. The agricultural credit (ACCFA) representative visited the barrios, on the average, almost four times as often as he had before, and the extension agent almost three times as often. These more frequent educational and service contacts in the village undoubtedly were a further reason

115

for the increase in agricultural production and the volume of products sold.

Local farm-to-market roads can contribute in many ways to agricultural development, more than is sometimes recognized. They are an essential part of the agricultural transportation network. Furthermore, they are a part that the people of a locality can often do something about for themselves if they receive leadership, some technical guidance, and a modest amount of financial assistance—and if enough of them become convinced that the benefits to them will be worth the effort.

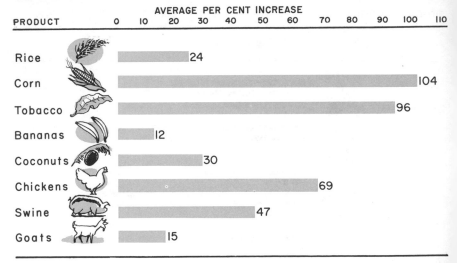

Average percentage increase in volume of sales of specific farm products after the construction of roads.

Long-Distance Transport

Long-distance transportation facilities are an equally essential part of the transportation network.

They are beyond the capacity of people in any one rural locality. Although they are essential for agricultural development they are needed by the whole country for a variety of other reasons as well. Consequently, many considerations have to be taken into account in determining their location. It is important that agricultural needs not be neglected in deciding what highways are to be built and where.

In the past, railways played an important part in long distance

116

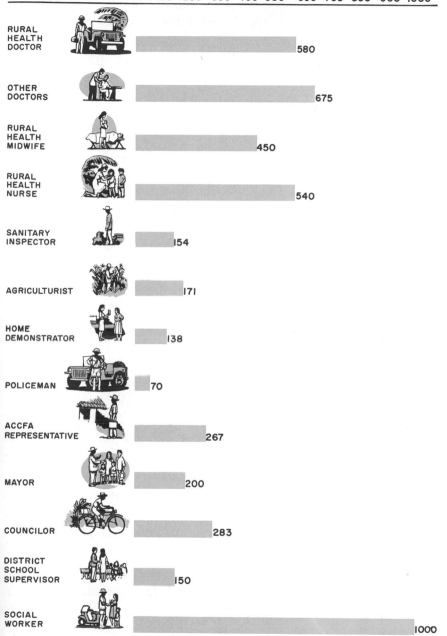

AVERAGE PER CENT INCREASE

OFFICIALS

| | 0 | 100 | 200 | 300 | 400 | 500 | 600 | 700 | 800 | 900 | 1000 |

RURAL HEALTH DOCTOR — 580

OTHER DOCTORS — 675

RURAL HEALTH MIDWIFE — 450

RURAL HEALTH NURSE — 540

SANITARY INSPECTOR — 154

AGRICULTURIST — 171

HOME DEMONSTRATOR — 138

POLICEMAN — 70

ACCFA REPRESENTATIVE — 267

MAYOR — 200

COUNCILOR — 283

DISTRICT SCHOOL SUPERVISOR — 150

SOCIAL WORKER — 1000

Average percentage increases in village visitations by selected officials after the construction of roads.

117

transport. They still do for regions that already have them. In more recent decades, truck transport has developed rapidly. In some places this is an addition to railways. In other places, it is a substitute for them.

Natural waterways—the seas and navigable inland rivers and lakes —offer less costly channels of transportation where they are available (and if speed is not too important). On the Central Plain of Thailand, the network of irrigation canals serves also as a transportation network. Boats carry products from farms to market towns and from market towns to the central markets of Bangkok.

Air transport, also, is sometimes used for agricultural transportation, but its high cost is justifiable chiefly in transporting highly perishable or valuable products, often between points otherwise inaccessible to one another. For example, it was for several years the practice to slaughter meat animals in the lowland eastern districts of Bolivia and fly the meat 300 miles to the city of La Paz, at an elevation of 14,000 feet, for sale to urban consumers the same day. Shipping frozen meat by air from inland slaughterhouses to refrigerated ships at seaports is a major industry in the Australian northwest.

There are many examples of substantial economic growth following the opening up of previously isolated areas by railroads or highways that have provided access to outside markets. One of these comes from Thailand, where a new paved highway was recently built from Bangkok into the upland country of the Northeast, a region formerly linked to Bangkok only by one old and inefficient railway. Maize production has multiplied very rapidly in the Northeast since the crop can be moved to Bangkok in trucks over the new highway. One-third of the entire maize production of Thailand now comes from that region. This increase was a major factor in making it possible for Thailand to earn more than $75,000,000 in foreign exchange by the export of maize in 1961-63.

Other new economic activities have been started in the region. Citrus orchards, banana plantations and small industries are increasing. Many people have moved into the region to take advantage of the new opportunities made possible by the highway. The county of Pakchong, halfway up the road, increased in population from 5,000 in the early 1950's to 65,000 in 1964.

118

These developments were not due solely to the new highway. The availability of an improved variety of maize and the presence of local merchants to handle the product played a large role in developing that crop. A concerted attack was made on malaria in the same period. Without the highway, however, none of these other developments could have brought about the degree of agricultural development that has occurred.

There are other cases, however, where expensive highways have been built but the hoped-for development did not follow—perhaps because the resources were not there to develop, perhaps because other essentials for development were not provided, sometimes simply because the highway, once built, was not maintained and soon fell into such disrepair that it no longer was economically usable.

Professor A. W. Ashby the eminent British agricultural economist, was fond of saying, "If I could do only one thing in a region to spur agricultural development, I would build roads. If to this I could add a second, I would build more roads. And if to these I could add a third, I would build still more roads." More than transportation alone is necessary for agricultural development, but it is one of the essentials.

A Transportation "System"

It cannot be emphasized too strongly that different kinds of local and long-distance transport facilities must add up to a well integrated *system* of transport. Not all highways need be paved. Paths, dirt roads, canals, highways, rivers and railways can all play a part. Some can be built and maintained by local effort, including local government. Some must be built and maintained by provincial and central authorities. All must be so connected and integrated with each other that products can move easily from farms to central markets, and so that supplies, equipment and services can reach the *farms,* not just the towns and villages, of the country.

This ends our discussion of the essentials of agricultural development: markets for farm products, constantly changing technology, local availability of farm supplies and equipment, production incen-

119

tives for farmers, and transportation.

With these, agriculture will move forward. Without any one of them, it will not.

Sometimes these are all available in only small parts of a country. In such cases, those parts of the country will experience agricultural development while the others will not. One item in a wise strategy for agricultural development is to make sure that these essentials are first made available in those parts of the country with the greatest agricultural potential. Later they can be gradually extended to other regions.

In concentrating on these essentials, the points discussed in Part I must not be overlooked. This is particularly true of those outlined in Chapter 3: The Farm. Farms frequently have to change in form, arrangement, and legal status in order that these "essentials" for agricultural development can have their full effect.

PART

The Accelerators of Agricultural Development

We turn now to five *accelerators* of agricultural development. There is an important difference between these and the "essentials" discussed in Part II. There can and will be some growth in agricultural productivity wherever all of the essentials are present but without *all* of them there will be none.

The case is different with the accelerators. Each of them is important but it is not indispensible. There can be agricultural development without one or more of them. Nevertheless, most countries need as rapid agricultural development as possible and to achieve this each of the accelerators can be of great help.

These accelerators are:

Education for Development (Chapter 10)
Production Credit (Chapter 11)
Group Action by Farmers (Chapter 12)
Improving and Expanding Agricultural Land (Chapter 13)
National Planning for Agricultural Development (Chapter 14)

121

CHAPTER 10

Education for Development

Is education an *essential* or only an *accelerator* of agricultural development?

Continuous *learning* certainly is an essential. But people learn from experience without being formally taught. Where transportation facilities are available many farmers move about. They visit cities and gain new knowledge and new ideas as a consequence. Where commercial arrangements for making farm supplies and equipment locally available are adequate, farmers see the fertilizers, seeds, implements and insecticides in the bazaars and market places, inquire about them, and a few begin to buy and use them. As other farmers see their neighbors using new supplies and equipment, they in turn learn about them and may learn how to use from these same experimenting neighbors. Where adequate marketing channels with local buying agents are present, offering to buy farm products at remunerative prices, some farmers go out of their way to learn how higher yields of these products can be secured. Thus, learning takes place even in the absence of formal provisions for education.

Formal arrangements for education *accelerate* this learning. Whether education is called an accelerator or an essential is not really important. A country does not have to have it in order to experience some slow rise in agricultural productivity, but no country in the world can be satisfied with that today. To accelerate agricultural development, education certainly is necessary.

Education for Development

Every human society has some arrangement for the training of children. This training gives each child the skills needed to live in his society. In addition, it may bring him up to date with respect to the past, transmitting to him the accumulated knowledge of his ancestors. Whether or not such education causes the more adventurous children to look forward inquiringly toward a different pattern of life in the future depends on the acquired knowledge and skills of their society or culture. Thus, general education of the young, trying to develop the capabilities of each child in line with the traditions of the society in which he was born, may or may not contain elements that make for development. It may advance development or it may be an obstacle to it.

By "education for development" we mean education that is appropriate for a society that wants to develop. It is education that is selective in its choice of materials for bringing each new generation up to date with respect to the past and is equally selective in the new knowledge, abilities and skills that it tries to help each person acquire. It is an education that puts greater stress on some of the historic beliefs and traditions of his society than it does on others. It is an education that draws on the past experience of other societies to the extent that this will help it move in the desired direction of development.

Education for People of All Ages

In a developing society education needs to be for people of all ages. In a traditional society, what those of each new generation are learning is the same that the older generation already knows and approves. Education for development, however, is a kind of education that introduces people to new knowledge, new skills, and new ways of doing things. These are different from the patterns of behavior of the older members of the society. If education for development is available only to the young, a conflict is introduced between the younger and the older members of the society: the new ways being learned by the young have to compete *against* the authority and the prestige of the elders.

Another reason why education for development must be for people of all ages is that in a rapidly developing society the technical competence needed by a man who is 30 or 40 or 50 years old is quite

Education for development includes the preparation of children for a lifetime of thinking scientifically about what they are doing, acquiring new knowledge, developing new skills and solving new problems.

different from that taught to him when he was young. Over and over, one hears the complaint that progress toward agricultural development is being obstructed by the poor training and inadequate ability of technicians and officials who are 35 to 60 years old. It is not their fault that the type of education available when they were young did not adequately prepare them for their responsibilities in later years. An important part of accelerating agricultural development is to make appropriate kinds of education for development available to such people throughout the period that they remain in active service.

Provision needs to be made for four types of education for development if agricultural development is to be accelerated as rapidly as possible:

1. Elementary and secondary education
2. Farmer education for development
3. Training of agricultural technicians
4. Urban education about agricultural development

Elementary and Secondary Education

What does each child need from elementary education to prepare him for life in a developing society? Does he not need, first, encouragement in developing an inquiring mind; second, confidence that he can master new knowledge and skills successfully; and third, stimulating knowledge of the world both within and beyond his village home? To achieve these objectives it may not be necessary to introduce new subjects of study. It does require careful selection of the materials used in teaching the traditional courses of reading, writing, arithmetic, geography, history, and literature. And it requires methods of teaching that recognize as their primary goal the three objectives suggested above.

Put in another way, at the stage of elementary schooling education for development consists of *beginning the preparation of children for a lifetime of thinking scientifically about what they are doing, acquiring new knowledge, developing new skills and solving new problems.* Secondary education should continue this same process.

From the standpoint of agricultural development, it is important that elementary education be made available to all rural children as

126

that secondary education be made available to
numbers of them. It is open to considerable
ther either elementary or secondary education
uld be very different from that for children in
Many children who attend rural schools will later
in cities. Some of those who go through urban
dary schools will later become agricultural tech-
others, who remain in the cities, will affect poli-
agricultural development through their attitudes
as citizens.

d learn about the growth of plants and animals.
t the rudiments of business: buying and selling,
sts and returns, the meaning of investments and
the methods of using natural resources wisely.
eral understanding of both agriculture and urban
each depends on the other.

taught the methods of scientific inquiry. Rural
to be encouraged to realize the possibility of vast
rming more productive and villages more modern.
the importance of farming to their country and
an honorable vocation. But it is doubtful that val-
ondary schools should be spent teaching boys the
nics of farming. It is more important for them to
nd the requirements for agricultural development
se farming practices presently in use but soon to be

elementary and secondary schools are not enough.
ols and colleges in low-income countries have been
r the years, at seeing young men and women, full
rgy, returning after graduation to village settings
nt departments dominated by their elders. Too fre-
der people have not been touched by new ideas or
need to be. The young cannot do the job alone with
osing them. They can make their contribution only if
g whom they live are also learning, growing, reach-
er ways.

128

rapidly as possible, an
constantly increasing
debate, however, whe
for rural children sho
the towns and cities. N
find themselves living
elementary and seco
nicians or officials. (
cies with respect to
and political action

All children shou
All should be taugh
how to calculate cc
the importance and
All should gain ger
industry and of ho

All need to be
young people need
changes making fa
They need to lear
to see farming as
uable time in sec
vocational mecha
come to understa
than to master th
out of date.

Even the best
Teachers in scho
disheartened, ov
of ideas and en
and to governm
quently these o
aspirations. The
their elders opp
the adults amor
ing out for bett

"All children should l

"All children should learn about the growth of plants and animals."

rapidly as possible, and that secondary education be made available to constantly increasing numbers of them. It is open to considerable debate, however, whether either elementary or secondary education for rural children should be very different from that for children in the towns and cities. Many children who attend rural schools will later find themselves living in cities. Some of those who go through urban elementary and secondary schools will later become agricultural technicians or officials. Others, who remain in the cities, will affect policies with respect to agricultural development through their attitudes and political action as citizens.

All children should learn about the growth of plants and animals. All should be taught the rudiments of business: buying and selling, how to calculate costs and returns, the meaning of investments and the importance and the methods of using natural resources wisely. All should gain general understanding of both agriculture and urban industry and of how each depends on the other.

All need to be taught the methods of scientific inquiry. Rural young people need to be encouraged to realize the possibility of vast changes making farming more productive and villages more modern. They need to learn the importance of farming to their country and to see farming as an honorable vocation. But it is doubtful that valuable time in secondary schools should be spent teaching boys the vocational mechanics of farming. It is more important for them to come to understand the requirements for agricultural development than to master those farming practices presently in use but soon to be out of date.

Even the best elementary and secondary schools are not enough. Teachers in schools and colleges in low-income countries have been disheartened, over the years, at seeing young men and women, full of ideas and energy, returning after graduation to village settings and to government departments dominated by their elders. Too frequently these older people have not been touched by new ideas or aspirations. They need to be. The young cannot do the job alone with their elders opposing them. They can make their contribution only if the adults among whom they live are also learning, growing, reaching out for better ways.

Farmer Education for Development

Since the abilities of farmers and the decisions they make about their farming operations are so crucial to the rate of agricultural development, special programs designed to facilitate farmer education are an important phase of education for development.

To be effective a program of farmer education should have eight characteristics:

It must go to farmers where they are. Unlike children whose primary occupation during the years they are in school is learning, the primary occupation of adult farmers is farming. This keeps them on the farm and at home most of the time. As a consequence, farmer education for development must go to them where they are: on their farms and in their home villages.

It must be specific to farmers' present interests and needs. It must be about topics in which farmers are already interested: how to increase crop and livestock production, how to increase the margin between cost and returns, how to improve the quality of living for their own families in their own communities.

It must respect the fact that farmers are adults. Children attend school at a time when they know they must grow up; they know they must change. They are in an atmosphere in which they are rewarded immediately when they learn and this encourages them to continue the process. Adults, however, usually feel that they are already supposed to know whatever their occupation calls for. Their learning and the mistakes they make in the process are not hidden in the classroom or the laboratory. Instead, they take place in full sight of other members of their family and their neighbors. Moreover, the rewards of their learning may be delayed for weeks or months until the results of the new knowledge and skills show up in greater agricultural production.

For these reasons the education of adults must be quite different from school education for young people. It must utilize special methods and be carried on in a particular way if it is to be effective.

It must be fitted into times when farmers are not too busy. Farmer education for development must take place during brief visits to farmers individually while they are in the field, in occasional meetings with groups of farmers at a time of the day or night when they are not in the field, or during off-seasons when their workload is light.

The unit of instruction for teaching and learning must in most cases be a particular new or changed practice. In schools and colleges, education is organized around general subjects of study. By contrast, most farmer education for development needs to be organized around specific new or changed practices of agricultural production: What is the new practice, why is it superior, how can it be carried out?

There are some exceptions to this rule. For farmers who have not had formal training in them, the specialized skills of farm management, including the planning of farm operations, skills of marketing and of administering cooperative societies are topics on which brief systematic periods of instruction are important. Short courses on machinery operation and maintenance have been used effectively in Nigeria, Greece, Colombia, and other places.

Technical training like the Congolese course for operating and maintaining farm equipment shown above is important to agricultural development, when added to good general education.

It must be accompanied by immediate opportunities for farmers to try out the new methods taught. This involves both the timeliness of the teaching and the availability of the supplies and equipment necessary to put each new method into practice. Any farmer education regarding fertilizer application needs to take place shortly before the season when fertilizer should be applied. And fertilizer must be available. Otherwise the only result of the teaching is frustration and wasted time.

Each new or changed practice proposed must be technically sound and economically profitable. To insure that this need is met, it is always desirable to run local trials to determine what the results would be if nearby farmers adopted the practice, and to make sure, by careful calculations, that returns from the new method will exceed the cost by a substantial amount. Three hundred farmers attending a field day at a research station in one country began asking questions about how much it cost to follow new methods being demonstrated to them, and what the market value of the crop would be. When the research worker in charge could not answer their questions, the farmers quickly lost interest.

Farmers need encouragement to experiment. The farmer who has acquired some new knowledge and skill still has to have considerable courage in order to try a new method for the first time. To reinforce his own desire to experiment he needs the personal support of a friend who encourages him. "Trying it out" is an important part of a farmer's education for development. This step is usually easier if he has a "teacher and friend" to support him.

Extension Education

The name widely given to farmer education for development based on the above principles is "extension education." It normally uses a distinctive group of teaching methods based on these principles. These teaching methods include conversations during farm and home visits, method demonstrations, result demonstrations, group meetings, farm tours, exhibits and fairs.

A frequent misunderstanding of the role of extension education is that "it is the task of extension education to take the results of agricultural research to farmers." Good extension workers do this, but it

131

The *result demonstration* shown above as a Morroccan extension worker explains the results of fertilizer trials on wheat to local farmers is an important extension teaching method. Below is an example of *drama* used in extension education. In this Indian scene the effects of nitrogen (Miss N), phosphate (Mr. P) and potassium (Mr. K) are being dramatized to show that all three are needed to give the best results.

would be more accurate to say that this part of their function is *to make farmers aware of the alternatives,* the different methods that exist for carrying on their farming operations.

Some of these alternatives already exist within the local community. Farmers at the present time are not all following the same practices. Some of them are more successful than others. Some strains of local seed are more productive than others. Some crops now being produced are more profitable than others. It is true that the results of new research widen these alternatives for the farmers of any community and are very important provided the necessary supplies and equipment can be obtained and the necessary new skills can be mastered. But it is a mistake to limit the concept of the extension worker to that of being an errand boy peddling news about new research. Instead, this part of the function of extension workers is to help farmers become aware of the opportunities that lie at hand, whether already practiced by someone in the local community or available from a research station.

The role of the extension worker that is most frequently ignored is his role as an "encouraging companion" of the farmer or farmers in any locality who would like to try one or more new methods, but who find themselves surrounded by other farmers urging them to follow traditional methods or waiting for an opportunity to make

fun of them if the new method fails. This role of the extension worker in encouraging the more adventurous is particularly important at early stages of development.

It is interesting that the French speaking Africans use the word *animateur* for an extension worker: he is the person who makes the farmer lively and active.

Training of Agricultural Technicians

Those of us who serve in one or another organization related to agriculture have a high calling. Agriculture is the biggest industry in the world and agricultural development is of primary importance today in practically all of the countries in which we work.

Elements of Professional Competence

Specialized technical knowledge and skills. Each of the jobs in which we are engaged calls for technical knowledge and specialized skills. Some of this we must have before we begin our work; some of it we gain on the job; some of it we can attain by reading, by private study, by thinking about our jobs and how we might do them better.

An understanding of agriculture. For each of us, it is important to have a general understanding of what agriculture is and how it operates, particularly in his own country. Books can help in this but they are no substitute for the increasing understanding that can come from getting personally acquainted with at least a few farmers, visiting farms of different kinds as frequently as we can, and listening to rural people talk about their various problems.

An understanding of the nature and importance of agricultural development. Understanding agricultural development is quite different from understanding agriculture itself. In addition to an understanding of agriculture, it involves a knowledge of how agriculture differs at different stages; of how each stage evolves into the next, and of what has to happen more widely within the country if such evolution is to take place.

An understanding of people and of organizations. It should be clear from the foregoing chapters that a great deal of agricultural development depends on changes in human behavior. Much of it depends on how one human being influences another. Other parts of it

134

depend on group action by a number of people working together.

It is not only among farmers and in rural communities that the quality of human relations is important. It is important in our dealings with colleagues within our own organizations. We are people, too, and some of the same factors that determine how farmers behave under different sets of circumstances affect the way we get along within our own organizations, whether in research stations, college classrooms, credit organizations, extension services, plant protection programs, or elsewhere in the wide range of activities related to agriculture. There is a great deal that we can learn that will help us to understand people and organizations better. Skill in human relations is an important part of the professional ability of each of us.

A realistic confidence in rural people. The farmer may not be a trained scientist, but he is usually a skilled cultivator. He may not be a statistician, but most farmers have a shrewd ability to judge risk and uncertainty. He is not an economist, but he can and does figure costs and returns.

The farmer is neither wiser nor more stupid than anyone else. He is a human being, and part of the professional skill of anyone working with farmers is to develop a good understanding of those areas in which the knowledge and ability of each farmer may be superior, and of those areas in which he may need help.

Respect for and understanding of specialists in other fields. Each of us tends to think that his particular specialty is the most important one. This is natural since we spend so much time pursuing it. It is even helpful to the degree that it may keep each of us enthusiastic about his own job. But it is not helpful when it keeps us from gaining a clear understanding of the contributions made by specialists in other fields and of how the success of our own activities depends on what these other specialists do. More and more we must learn to work together.

Personal effectiveness within an organization. Most of us work in large organizations. Every large organization has to have standard methods of procedure. Because the regulations are so numerous, the tendency is to become absorbed by these and not to see or act beyond them. The regulations of an organization are the skeleton that keeps the different parts of it working satisfactorily with each other. For the organization to be effective, this skeleton must be overlaid by good human relations and by a positive will to use the organization to accomplish the wider purpose for which it was founded.

Constant learning and experimentation. None of us will ever know enough to do his job the way it ought to be done. Most of us know a good deal to begin with; the problem is to keep learning.

Professional skill for the agricultural technician, therefore, cannot be narrow, nor can it be acquired early in one's career to last the rest of a lifetime. It includes as much as one can learn about the physical world of sun, soils, rain, plants and animals; it involves all that one can learn about people and about the ways in which they work together; it involves all that one can learn about learning itself and about how society has changed, is changing, and can be changed. It requires an inquiring mind and a scientific spirit throughout one's active life.

None of this breadth of understanding is a substitute for specialized knowledge and skills related to the particular task each of us is asked to perform. It can, however, contribute to the effectiveness with which each of us does his own job and it can contribute as well to the satisfaction each derives from his career.

University Education and Training

Primarily, the role of a college of agriculture is to educate and train persons who intend to spend their careers as technicians or officials in activities related to agriculture. Only a minority of the graduates of colleges of agriculture in every country become farmers or professional farm managers. A much larger number enter other activities related to farming: research, teaching, agricultural credit, the manufacture or distribution of farm equipment and supplies, or administration of a great variety of activities related to agriculture.

Whether a particular graduate is himself to be a farmer or is to engage in one of these other activities, it is the primary function of his university education to get him started on the road of *problem-solving related to agriculture,* to give him an initial fund of knowledge with which to begin, and to teach him how to acquire more knowledge and additional skills. In order to fulfill this function the content of university education in agriculture needs to include attention to

136

all of the elements of professional skill discussed in the preceding section of this chapter.

It is not, or should not be, the function of a college of agriculture to cram students full of detailed knowledge to be used in later years. How to *use* knowledge and new skills should be as important a concern of university education as the knowledge and skills themselves. Consequently, colleges of agriculture should place even more emphasis on practice in the use of problem-solving skills than they do on the knowledge and skills themselves.

To fulfill this function, the college of agriculture, staff members and students alike, needs to be "a community of learners." Staff members themselves must be intent on learning and problem-solving if they are to give their students the kind of education and training they need and have a right to expect.

Undergraduate education in a college of agriculture should not be expected to do the whole job of specific vocational training for any of the large number of careers related to agriculture. Instead, it should give a broad understanding of agriculture and of agricultural development, and instill a scientific spirit and habit of mind with respect to the many elements of professional competence its students will need later on. Some specialization in such broad fields as plant science, animal science, agricultural economics, agricultural engineering, and rural education is good. It allows students to spend relatively more time on the kinds of problems in which they are most interested, and it begins, although it cannot finish, their specialized training for different professional careers.

Induction Training

After a student has graduated from a college of agriculture and is employed to fill a particular position he usually needs more specific training for that particular job. For certain positions, it may be possible to satisfy this need in a few days while for other positions it may require a period of several weeks or months. In some instances such training is most effectively handled by the agency employing the person. In others, it is best handled by a special institute giving induction training for a number of different agencies (as is done for a number of banks and credit agencies by the Agricultural Credit and Cooperatives Institute of the University of the Philippines).

In-Service Training

To accelerate agricultural development it is important that each technician continue to have opportunities to learn, develop new skills and increase his specialized competence as long as he is in active service. Formal in-service training is particularly important for technicians for whom the knowledge and the skills that they need to use are changing rapidly from year to year (extension agents, research workers, and teachers). It is also of special importance for technicians who have not had university education or adequate induction training, or for those who had these many years ago. In most cases, it is not feasible (even if it were desirable) to replace poorly trained technicians by younger ones with more adequate university education. Instead, a well designed and intensive program of in-service training can usually upgrade the competence of such persons to a satisfactory level. The faster agricultural development is taking place, the greater the need for in-service training.

The experience of an extension project of the Allahabad Agricultural Institute in India provides a striking illustration of the effect of in-service training. This project was started by employing a group of extension workers none of whom had had any previous experience in agricultural extension work. Some were high school graduates, some were graduates of practical schools of agriculture and some were university graduates. All were given only ten days of induction training. An in-service training program consisting of two days every second week was begun and continued for the first 18 months. After that, the pattern was changed to two days every three weeks. By the third year of the program, there was no difference in the level of performance among the three groups with differing school and university training; the in-service training had made up for what differences there were in the beginning.

Rewards for Increasing Competence

Our emphasis in this section has been on formal arrangements for helping agricultural technicians and officials gain the increasing com-

138

petence they need for their work. It should not be ignored, however, that persons engaged in any activity may learn even when there are no formal arrangements for teaching them. They can learn from experience and they can, if they will, increase their competence through private study and personal experimentation.

Technicians and officials need *incentives* to keep increasing their competence as long as they are active. The most important of these incentives is recognition of increasing competence in the form of higher salaries. A second is the prospect of promotion to positions of increased responsibility. Still another is the degree of freedom that each person has in pursuing his task. If officials do not welcome innovations by their subordinates and do not welcome suggestions as to how the whole program might be improved, the more able persons in subordinate positions in the agency will see little point in increasing their competence either through study or through experimentation.

Thus, the policies of any agency with respect to salaries, promotions, and personal freedom to innovate and to make suggestions arc vital factors in the lifelong growth and competence of technicians and officials.

Urban Education About Agricultural Development

Frequently one hears it said that what is needed to spur agricultural development is not so much to train farmers as to educate city people.

It is certainly true that people who have political power and influence have a profound effect on the rate of agricultural development. Many of them do not understand what is necessary for agricultural development, or even why agricultural development is important to the country as a whole.

Most of them are city people. They live closer together, where it is easier for them to exercise political influence. They have interests of their own which frequently conflict in the short run with steps that need to be taken to spur agricultural development. Whereas farmers may need higher prices for their products in order to have adequate incentives to increase production, people in the cities are interested in paying lower prices for food. Increasing agricultural production always requires substantial investment in rural roads, storage facilities, irrigation and a variety of government services serving agriculture, but urban people are more aware of the need for industrial investment to increase employment opportunities in the cities. Unless it is pointed out to them, they are not likely to realize how agricultural development increases the market for industrial products and for the commercial services that the town and cities provide. Many of them are unaware that certain kinds of industries—particularly those that provide supplies and equipment needed by farmers and those that process agricultural products—are of greater benefit to the total economy than certain other kinds of industrial development.

What can be done to educate city people with respect to agricultural development? Very little has been done, or is known, about this. One method might be to see that certain courses in high schools and colleges, especially courses in economics and sociology, give adequate attention to the rural problems of the country and to the role of agriculture in the total economy. Another might be a combination of newspaper stories, radio programs, and newsreels in movie theaters. These could give news of rural problems and progress. They could present the case for agricultural development and the methods that can be used to achieve it. They could explore the dependence of agriculture and industry on each other. To have an effective adult urban educational program of this kind it is probable that some special agency of the government would have to devote its full attention to this particular task.

For education to be an accelerator of agricultural development it needs to develop inquiring minds, a confidence that most problems can be solved, and scientific habits of thought and action. These purposes must permeate school and college education at all levels. Such education is equally important for adults on their farms and in their villages, and for technicians and administrators in every activity related to agriculture. Agricultural development requires that people keep growing, developing new skills and mastering new knowledge throughout their active careers.

Even urban adults need to keep learning about agricultural development because of the many ways in which they influence the opportunities and incentives of farmers and farm families.

CHAPTER 11

Production Credit

Efficient agencies extending production credit to farmers can be an important accelerator of agricultural development. To produce more, farmers must *spend* more—on improved seeds, pesticides, fertilizers and implements. Such expenditures must be financed either out of savings or by borrowing for the period between the date when supplies and equipment must be purchased and the time when the harvests can be sold.

It is frequently argued that borrowing is the only way to meet this need because of the poverty of many farmers. There is some truth in this, but it can be exaggerated. Even in regions where many farmers are very poor there are others who do have some savings. It is usually these farmers who are better off who will, in any case, be the first to adopt new practices not just because they have the money but because they are more alert and progressive. Moreover, the fact that farmers frequently decline to purchase a new input, saying "I don't have the money" can be misleading. Such a statement is a convenient way to end an argument even among people who are not poor. The person's real reason may be quite different. Where this argument is used to justify not buying improved seeds or fertilizers the real reason frequently is (1) that the farmer is not convinced that the new input would be technically effective, or (2) that he feels that the increased product to be had from the use of the new input would not be worth its cost plus the added labor of using it, or (3) that the increased output promised by the use of the inputs is not large enough to be worth the gamble of trying out a new method. Meeting these legitimate arguments by developing new technology that will raise production by a large amount, and by a widespread program of local testing of these supplies, is always more important than increasing credit facilities.

The other frequent argument for establishing *new* credit agencies is that prevailing interest rates are too high. They undoubtedly *are* high when compared with rates for similar credit in more advanced economies and for urban industrial loans. Part of the reason for higher interest rates for agricultural production credit, at early stages of agricultural development, may lie in a greater scarcity of capital in developing economies where even urban industrial loans involve interest rates of 10 to 15% and sometimes even more. Another part of the reason is the higher costs of administering many small loans to many farmers scattered over a wide area. Such costs have to be borne one way or another, either by setting interest rates high enough to cover them or by admittedly subsidizing the cost of production credit to farmers.

Whether interest rates are "too high" also depends on what is readily available to purchase with the borrowed money. If $50 spent on fertilizer will increase the value of the harvest six months later by $150, a farmer could well afford to pay even 100% interest for the six-month's period ($25), because he would still gain $75 by the transaction. On the other hand, if $50 spent on "improved" seed will only increase the value of the harvest by $65 an interest rate of 10% might be considered too high in view of the added factor of uncertainty about the weather and the harvest.

In other words, how "reasonable" a rate of interest is depends partly on the economic value of supplies and equipment that are available locally. It depends also on the cost of making the loans and collecting them, and such costs are higher for small loans to widely scattered farmers than they are for big loans in urban centers. It depends, third, on the extent to which loans are repaid in full and on time, for what we normally call the rate of interest covers losses due to non-repayment as well as the costs of administration and a fee

142

The further agricultural development proceeds, the more farmers use production credit.

for the use of the money for the period of the loan.

Production credit at reasonable rates of interest can be helpful, but it is no substitute for new technology capable of raising production *substantially*. Many farmers have some savings, and many others can afford to pay even high rates of interest to present sources of credit if the supplies and equipment available for purchase are highly productive.

Having said this, however, it remains true that efficiently administered programs of production credit are an important accelerator of agricultural development, and such credit is used by progressive farmers more and more as agriculture advances.

Learning to Use Production Credit

Many farmers have borrowed frequently to meet urgent family needs, and many of them do not like to borrow unless it is absolutely necessary. They may not recognize the difference between borrowing

143

for consumption, where the loan does not increase future production, and borrowing for production, for purposes that provide increased income out of which to repay the loan.

The practice of borrowing and lending for consumption puts three obstacles in the way of using production credit. First, it makes borrowing seem to be something to be avoided if at all possible. Second, it tends to establish interest rates at a high level since it is the less provident persons who need to borrow for consumption, and their future ability to pay is doubtful. Third, it does not recognize the soundness of *future production plans* as an element in the creditworthiness of a borrower.

Effective production credit requires the removal of these obstacles. It depends on the use of credit being viewed as a normal part of efficient farm operation. It depends on interest rates geared to the actual cost of providing production credit that usually guarantees its own repayment through the increased income it makes possible.

It is a major step for farmers to move from their reluctance to borrow for consumption purposes to a recognition that borrowing to purchase additional inputs can be profitable and should be encouraged.

To help farmers take this step it is necessary both to have production credit made easily available to them and to give them guidance in how to use it.

Types of Production Credit

Sale of supplies and equipment on credit to be repaid in farm produce. This kind of production credit has been used effectively in many countries. It has the advantage of relieving the farmer of uncertainty about the price which he can get for his harvest out of which to repay the loan in cash. He may purchase seed or fertilizer, knowing how much grain or other produce he must give in payment for it after harvest-time.

Supervised credit. This combines production credit with technical help to the farmer using it. An agent first helps the farmer to make a production plan for his farm business for the coming year. The plan includes the amounts of seeds, fertilizers, implements, etc., to be purchased, and the cost of each. It may include an estimate of the

The ACAR program in Brazil combines credit supervision with extension education. The agricultural credit agent and the home demonstration agent visit farm families together.

amount to be spent on hired labor. It includes an estimate of the amount of credit needed to finance these expenditures and the probable value of the increased harvest.

On the basis of this farm plan, credit is extended to the farmer either in cash or in the form of the specific supplies and equipment needed. The credit agent visits the farmer from time to time, helping him use efficiently the supplies and equipment financed by the loan. *The security for the loan is the estimated value of the harvest.*

In some programs of supervised credit, if the farmer and his family are likely to need consumption credit within the year this is included also as part of the plan for the year, thereby making it unnecessary for the farm family to turn to other lenders.

While supervised credit programs can be very effective, they depend on having highly-skilled agents who really know the problems of farming in the region and who can realistically assess the need for, and the probable returns from using, new inputs. The supervision must be competent and frequent if it is to justify the extra cost that is involved.

Agricultural banks. Agricultural banks operate very much like urban commercial banks, but are set up primarily to advance production credit to farmers. They vary in form and in procedures from country to country. They are more helpful to farmers who have already learned to use production credit wisely than they are to farmers who are just learning to do this. They seldom have as many branches or are located in as many places as rapid agricultural development requires.

The Rural Banks of the Philippines are one form of agricultural bank. They are located in small communities throughout the countryside where they are convenient to farmers. They can borrow funds from central banks to increase the number and amount of their loans to farmers. They accept deposits from local depositors, both farmers and non-farmers. They make loans locally, including loans for agricultural credit. Similar agricultural banks are found in many countries.

A practice that effectively combines the advantages of agricultural banks with those of supervised credit is possible in localities having both farseeing private lenders and a public program of extension education. Extension workers can help farmers prepare production and financial plans for their farms, then recommend to private lenders or to agricultural banks that they make loans available to individual farmers on the basis of these farm plans. Then, after the loans have been made, the extension workers can help the farmers use the loans wisely. One effective example of this is to be found in Argentina. Another is the lending policies of a branch of the Philippine Banking Corporation at Tanauan, Luzon, and the Farm and Home Development Program of the College of Agriculture, University of the Philippines. The Farm and Home Development Program identifies particularly profitable production enterprises and practices for farm operators in the area, and the bank makes production loans to farm operators who are receiving extension guidance from the College.

Cooperative credit societies. Many efforts have been made to establish cooperative credit societies to meet farmers' needs for production credit. Some of these have been successful. Many others have not been. They most frequently succeed when they are established among educated farmers who have had considerable successful experience in using production credit provided through other channels. If they are true cooperatives they add complicated management problems unfamiliar to the farmer members. Where special governmental regulations and controls are introduced in an attempt to meet these complicated management problems, the societies are "cooperative" in name only. They are really much more a kind of agricultural bank.

At early stages, before farmers have become skilled in using production credit, it is simpler, and usually more effective, to have a system which allows farmers to learn this skill of using production credit wisely on their farms, without at the same time having to learn the different and equally complicated skills of managing a cooperative society.

Production credit by private lenders. Most production credit used by farmers is provided by private lenders, certainly until relatively late in the process of development. Members of the family, merchants, landlords (in some cases), and local private money lenders supply this credit.

For private sources of production credit to be used effectively, it is important that the distinctions between production and consumption credit be clearly recognized. Interest rates and loan periods appropriate for production credit need to be established.

Even after other sources of production credit become available, farmers frequently continue to borrow from private lenders to buy production supplies and equipment. They often find it simpler, and they do it partly because they are accustomed to turning to these lenders for consumption credit to tide them over until the harvest.

Desirability of Alternative Sources of Credit

Whatever type of production credit may be introduced or encouraged in any particular region it is better for each farmer to have a choice among two or more sources of credit. Much of the abuse of lending arises where the farmer must borrow from a single available source or not at all.

Too frequently, dissatisfaction with private lenders leads to attempts to eliminate them and replace them entirely with a new single source of credit, perhaps an agricultural bank or a cooperative society. This may or may not prove to be more satisfactory. It is almost always less satisfactory than having two or more sources of credit among which farmers may choose. With two or more sources of credit, each one bids for the farmers patronage by making its interest rates and its method of making loans as reasonable as good financial practice can allow. Consequently, each farmer is less likely to feel that he is being exploited by the lender with whom he chooses to deal, whether private, governmental, or cooperative.

Problems of the Farm Operator with Respect to Production Credit

What are the considerations farm operators must take into account in deciding whether to borrow for productive purposes?

Estimate of the probable yield. The farm operator has to predict the yield of the crop or livestock involved, with and without the use of the additional inputs that credit would allow him to use. In part, his estimate can be based on the results of local testing and his own past experience. He must also consider variations in the weather. If he knows that the weather in his locality is quite different from year to year he will be less likely to risk the investment of borrowed funds.

Estimate of the market price of his crop at harvest time. If, in his experience, the price fluctuates violently the farmer will be less willing to incur cash obligations to repay loans. In a manner pointed out earlier, the Joint Commission on Rural Reconstruction in Taiwan has met this problem by "lending" the physical inputs themselves to farmers, with repayment to be made in a given number of physical units of the crop, regardless of market prices.

Cost of the credit. While farm operators could frequently afford to pay quite high interest rates in order to get access to production supplies and equipment they naturally will be inclined to use credit much more freely if interest rates and other charges are low.

148

Possible penalties for default. In view of uncertainties about the weather and about market prices at harvest time, a farm operator thinking of using production credit must always consider what would happen if he could not pay the loan when due. He is particularly unlikely to take this risk if he has to give land or other property as security. He is more likely to borrow if the security for the loan is a lien on the particular crop, as it should be. This is a more appropriate security for production loans than is land.

Ease of availability of the credit. The farm operator who is sufficiently alert and progressive to consider using production credit is a busy man. He has neither time nor inclination to make repeated trips to distant offices in order to get a small loan. Furthermore, as a businessman he is annoyed by petty regulations and office procedures. Consequently, sources of production credit need to be *close* to farmers, procedures need to be as *simple* as possible, and persons who process loan requests need to be *helpful* and *courteous*. Farmers' reasons for continuing to borrow at high rates of interest from local lenders often include this matter of the ease or difficulty in getting the loan.

Timeliness. Just as in the cases of seeds and fertilizer, farmers need to be able to get credit precisely when they need it.

Problems of the Lending Agency

Lenders, also, have special problems with respect to production credit in the earlier stages of development.

High administrative costs in making and collecting loans. This is the biggest, and an inevitable, problem of production credit agencies, particularly in making loans to small farm businesses in the early stages of agricultural development. The amount of credit any one farm operator needs in a particular season is small, and there are many, many farm operators scattered at considerable distances from each other who could effectively use production credit. Yet it costs a lender about as much in time and effort to grant or to collect a small loan as a large one, so his costs for a given total volume of loans in the form of many small loans are much higher than if the same amount of money were lent to fewer borrowers.

149

There are two ways to meet this problem. One is to subsidize the administrative costs of providing production credit. The other is to combine credit services with one or more other services requiring frequent contact with the same people (borrowers), since this may substantially reduce the administrative cost of providing the credit. An important advantage of a program of supervised credit is that it combines credit and extension education in a manner by which the same visits to farmers can serve both purposes.

Appropriate loan periods. It is customary for consumption loans to be made "until harvest-time." This is satisfactory for some production loans as well, but not for all. It is suitable for loans for the purchase of seeds, for pesticides, and frequently for fertilizers. Repayment of production loans for such purposes should fall due not too soon (but not too long) after the crop is harvested. From the farm operator's standpoint, he should repay the loan as soon as he can without being forced to sell his crop immediately after harvest, when prices are usually lowest. In this connection, measures to prevent excessive seasonal price fluctuations for farm products are particularly important.

In the case of loans for buying livestock, implements, and other items of equipment a longer loan period is usually necessary, with repayment over a period of several years, and in installments timed to correspond to normal dates for selling farm produce. Calculation of such loan periods involves a new skill that lenders have to acquire for the efficient management of production loans.

Payment in full on agreed due-dates. Lenders of funds to meet consumption loans frequently do not insist on repayment of the principal of the loan in full at the time it is due, provided the interest is paid in full and some payment is made on the principal. Some lenders even prefer that the total of the principal not be repaid; they would prefer to continue to have a claim on the borrower's future income at an agreed high interest rate.

Production credit requires definite due-dates, and it requires that each loan be repaid on time, presumably out of the enhanced harvest which the loan helped to make possible—except in case of crop failures beyond the control of the farmer, when an extension of the repayment period is justified and even necessary.

150

When new agencies are set up specifically to provide production credit this matter of time of repayment presents a real problem. Private lenders are less likely to insist on prompt repayment, on time and in full, so farm operators frequently prefer to use private sources even where new agencies offer production credit at lower interest rates. For the good of farm operators themselves, it is important that the habit be established of repaying production loans on time and *in full*. Only so can the use of production credit be an advantage rather than an obstacle to agricultural development. If each farm operator learns to pay each loan when it is due he establishes a reputation for "credit-worthiness" that makes it easier for him to secure other loans in the future. If he does not, he closes the door on himself.

Assessing Credit Costs and Demand

One common mistake is to set up a new production credit agency without thorough assessment of the need for it and the problems it would face. This assessment should answer at least three questions:

1. What is the nature and the extent of the *need* for production credit? Here the most important factor is: what locally-tested, reliable and effective purchasable inputs are or can be made readily available to how many farm operators? Next, to what extent can farm operators finance these requisites without borrowing? This depends partly on how costly each input is, and the amount of it that a farm operator can, in the beginning, use effectively. It depends partly, also, on how close to the margin of subsistence those farm operators most willing to try the new practices now live.

2. What sources of credit are now available to farm operators? Credit for consumption is already available almost universally. In many cases this source may be adequate to meet the need for the relatively small production loans of those farm operators who must have production credit in order to make their first purchase of inputs. This is one point at which an extension education program for present *lenders* may deserve serious consideration. If they can be helped to understand the special needs and conditions for *production* credit, and the future expanded service to be rendered in this field, a program of extension education for them at this stage may be the most feasible

151

and effective first step in making production credit available to farm operators.

3. What costs and administrative problems will the new production credit agency probably have? Here the problems of lenders discussed above are involved and deserve careful assessment. While some of this assessment can be achieved by an attempt to calculate costs in advance, serious errors (usually *underestimates* of costs and problems) are inevitable by this method alone. Experimental projects of modest size, in localities where extension education is operating and where potential agricultural productivity is high, are necessary in order to accurately assess the costs and problems of an expanded credit program.

———————

We must keep in mind that the purpose of production credit is to enable farmers to purchase productive equipment and supplies. Credit is therefore less important to agricultural development than is the ready availability of such supplies and equipment at convenient nearby markets. But where effective and profitable production supplies and equipment are available nearby, and where farmers have facilities for learning how to use them, production credit can accelerate the adoption of improved practices.

CHAPTER 12

Group Action by Farmers

Individual farmers make most of the decisions about what is produced on their farms and about the methods of cultivation and the supplies and equipment used.

At the other extreme, the actions of governments have an enormous influence on the opportunities open to individual farmers and on farmers' awareness of these opportunities, as they make their decisions.

Between these extremes of individual decision and government action there is a third kind of activity important in accelerating agricultural development. This is voluntary group action by farmers within local communities and often also throughout a region or even a whole nation.

Some group action by farmers occurs informally. Farmers work together in planting their crops or in harvesting or threshing them. They cooperate in helping farmers who fall ill. They join together in meeting sudden disasters: floods, wind storms, invasion by locusts or other destructive pests.

Sometimes groups of farmers move beyond these kinds of cooperation to take joint action in a more organized way, and over longer periods of time, in order to meet needs that many of them recognize but cannot meet by acting alone. They may join together in building a road, in digging an irrigation well, in maintaining irrigation channels, in marketing their crops, in cooperatively arranging for the purchase of supplies and equipment or for the purpose of extending credit to one another.

Group action often occurs in some societies, for traditional purposes, without participation of anyone from outside the group. Most farmers are so busy with the problems of their own farms, however, that unless someone encourages them to join together in group action for new purposes, and helps them make the necessary arrangements, they do not act together as much as would be to their advantage. Group action on developmental projects requires specialized skills that may have to be learned. Hence systematic stimulation and assistance to group action can be an important accelerator of agricultural development.

Types of Group Action

Construction of community facilities. Many local needs of farming communities can be met by group action in which the chief requirement is labor. The construction of unpaved roads, wells, and simple irrigation and drainage channels is an example. The construction of school buildings, clinics, or community centers requires more materials, but chiefly of kinds that are locally available and can often be paid for by voluntary contributions from the group.

In South Vietnam a group of farmers, working together, cleared ten acres of unused land with the aid of a government owned bulldozer, built an access road to a nearby highway, and constructed a new school. They worked out among themselves a formula whereby each farm family provided a proportionate share of the labor and materials.

Control of common pests. Rats, predatory birds, and many kinds of insects are pests that individual farmers can seldom deal with effectively; common action is needed by everyone in the locality, or even throughout a wide region. Although voluntary group action can help meet this problem, some degree of compulsion is usually necessary because control measures must cover the entire area if they are to be effective, whether every farm operator wishes to cooperate or not.

Formal cooperative organizations. Group action on certain other problems requires more formal and continuing organization. Cooperative societies are a common example. Cooperatives are usually organized to undertake one or more of four functions: the marketing

Cooperatives may take many forms and perform varied functions. Mexican villagers are assembled in front of the cooperative store they have organized with the help of students from a UN school.

of agricultural products, the purchase of farm supplies and equipment, the provision of credit to individual farmers, or actual production on a cooperative farm. Each of these types of cooperative has its own special problems; all of them involve complex problems of administration.

In only a few countries are cooperative societies wholly voluntary. Membership is voluntary in many instances. In other cases, a degree of compulsion is involved with respect to membership, particularly if such things as fertilizer or irrigation water are made available only to members of the society. The management of cooperative societies is seldom completely in the hands of their members. In many instances the form of administration of cooperatives is rigidly controlled by government regulations and sometimes the societies are actually administered by government agencies. At the very least, official regulations set the limits within which cooperative societies can function, and the laws governing them often prescribe in considerable detail how they must be managed.

It cannot be taken for granted that just because farmers engage in a few cultivation practices together, or join in building houses, it will be easy and natural for them to organize and operate cooperative societies. The skills and understanding required are quite different.

Local self-government. Every organized society has local arrangements for governing certain aspects of the life of the people. However, these are more likely to be arrangements for maintaining law and order than for undertaking and administering development projects. Taxes are collected almost everywhere, but they normally flow to central governments that then decide how they are to be used. Local people frequently have little or no control over the amount of taxes collected or what the taxes they pay are used for.

In most parts of the world, farmers do not have the kind of local self-government that gives them the power to tax themselves, to decide on the use of these funds, and to employ people to carry out projects they would like their local government to sponsor. Yet this kind of group action can enable farmers to tackle jointly many things needed for development. They can establish schools; they can build and maintain roads; they can maintain irrigation facilities; they can, if they wish, employ extension agents.

Local self-government is at least as important to the political development of a people as it is to agricultural or other economic development. If governmental decisions are all made in some distant capital, citizens generally have little opportunity to learn how government operates, what it can do, and what it cannot do. On the other hand, if some decisions are made by local governments, citizens have a much better opportunity to become politically mature, and they have some of the resources of governmental action in their own hands to apply as they see fit to a variety of local problems. The central government can then deal with the broader problems that need to be faced on a national scale.

Political action by farmers. In a number of countries agricultural development has been accelerated by farmers through group action to bring political pressure on the government to act on matters af-

156

fecting agriculture. There are always conflicts of interest between different groups in a country. Farmers want high prices for their products, while urban people want low prices for their food. Farmers want to buy supplies and equipment at low prices, while manufacturers and importers want to sell at high prices. Large landholders want to keep all the land they have, while small farmers want more and those without land want farms of their own.

At various times and places farmers have organized to try to influence agricultural prices, to influence land tenure policy, to influence taxation policy, or to win for themselves a more active role in the political process itself. Such farmers' action groups have the same justification as do chambers of commerce, associations of manufacturers, and political action by labor unions or by any other group. Whether political action actually accelerates agricultural development at a particular time depends on the wisdom of the objectives of the group and on the means that they adopt to try to achieve their objectives.

Stimulating Group Action

Four kinds of activities can be undertaken to stimulate appropriate group action by farmers:

1. Help in organizing
2. Furnishing special materials
3. Technical and managerial assistance
4. Financial assistance

Help in organizing. Whether the project is building a road, controlling rats, or setting up a marketing cooperative, farmers may need help in organizing for group action. If it is a type of undertaking with which they have had no previous experience, they may not know what kind of organization it requires. They may be unable to analyze the problems involved or to judge the feasibility of the proposed project.

A competent person from outside the community who has the confidence of the local people can help them think through these matters. To do this he must be competent with respect to the kind of project being considered *and* about the requirements for effective group organization and action. Such a person can guide farmers away from

157

projects that are not feasible, or he can help them get the kinds of assistance from the outside that will make the project feasible. Often he can help them come to a decision about things they want that might be undertaken by group action.

Another sort of assistance that such a person can often give is to bring together persons interested in a common problem but who are kept apart by local patterns of status or prestige. He can provide initial leadership. He may also be able to identify from within the group individuals who are capable of leadership but are reluctant to accept this responsibility unless encouraged to do so.

Furnishing special materials. Local groups may agree upon the need for an improvement, but may not have certain materials or equipment that it requires and may not know how to obtain them. Local roads, for example, may require culverts if the roads are not to wash out in rainy weather or if valuable fields are not to be flooded. In the self-help road program in the Philippines, referred to on page 114 the central government provided bulldozers for some of the heavy grading. Group action for insect and disease control on fruit trees has been stimulated in many places by helping groups obtain sprayers capable of reaching the higher branches of the trees.

Sometimes all that is needed is to point out to the group where the necessary materials or equipment can be obtained. In other cases it is necessary actually to obtain the materials and arrange for their transportation to the place where they are needed.

Technical and managerial assistance. Effective group action may be prevented by lack of technical knowledge or the skills needed for management of the undertaking. Again in the Philippines, many local communities are separated from towns and markets by steep-banked streams that are difficult to cross. People in some communities have attempted to bridge the streams, but have become discouraged because their bridges washed away in the first high water. Technical engineering assistance has been given a number of such communities in designing and building bridges capable of withstanding floods. (Assistance has also been given in obtaining cement, steel, large timbers, or other materials required for constructing durable bridges.)

In discussing farmer cooperative associations in this and the preceding chapter the need for trained and efficient management has been emphasized. Local groups wishing to form cooperative organizations almost always need help, first in learning to understand the need for competent management, and then in locating qualified managers or training persons for the job.

Financial assistance. There are many cases where groups of farmers are willing to contribute their labor and even some money to a project, but the cash costs of the projects are beyond their resources. This has given rise in many countries to the practice of "grants-in-aid" from the central government to meet part of the cost of local projects. Sometimes these local projects are carried out by voluntary groups; at other times by local governments. Such grants-in-aid are a recognition of the contribution that the project can make to the community and through it to the national life. They demonstrate the interest of the central government in local development, but at the same time recognize that the central government cannot do everything— that the people must likewise make an effort. They are thus a wholesome way to combine the resources of the local community with those of the national government so that more rapid development can be achieved than could be accomplished by either set of resources alone.

"Community Development"

Many "community development" programs specialize in stimulating group action along the lines outlined in the foregoing section. In such programs, group projects are the main activity. A trained community development worker is provided to help local people select a project and organize to carry it out. He himself provides, or calls in, the skilled assistance that is required. He helps the group obtain the necessary materials. He may help them obtain a grant-in-aid.

Such "community development" projects may contribute directly to speeding up agricultural development by providing important public facilities such as roads, storage facilities, or irrigation channels. Other community development projects may affect agricultural development only indirectly. They may increase the amenities for village living, thereby making it more attractive. They may begin the process of home improvement by providing pure water supplies or public

Community development programs help local people to organize and carry out projects which they think are needed. An Afghan community development worker discusses conditions and problems with local leaders.

drains, and this may lead to a rise in the aspirations of farm families, increasing the people's desire for other improvements in their way of living that require money and therefore increase their incentive to increase agricultural production. The experience of progress may change social values in the direction that makes innovation by individual farmers more acceptable to the local community.

Perhaps the most important effect of such community development programs is in giving local groups some experience in working together on projects of their own choice. By undertaking one group project after another, people come to realize that they can meet many of their problems without waiting for action by the central government. They also acquire the skills of organization that help equip them to operate local government geared to the acceleration of development.

To "Get the Job Done."

Some people talk as though there were some special virtue in group action as such. Some others see particular merit in action by individuals. There is some truth in each point of view. Both should be considered when making a decision as to how a particular task should be undertaken. The proper question to ask in each case is: "How can this particular task best be accomplished at this particular time, among these particular people?"

There was a time when American farmers joined together in building barns. Later, when dimensioned lumber became available, it became easily possible for the individual farmer to build his own barn, and the cooperative "barn-raisings" ceased. The same thing happened to the ancient form of group work parties, the *combuite,* in Haiti. Before effective local self-government is established, voluntary group action to build roads is advantageous. Later, it may become more convenient to use hired labor paid through local taxation. There are many circumstances under which it is easier to improve existing private marketing channels than to replace them by the group action of new marketing cooperatives.

Voluntary action by groups of farmers is one of the accelerators of agricultural development when applied to those pressing problems which, at the particular moment, group action can best meet.

CHAPTER 13

Improving and Expanding Agricultural Land

Most of the measures for agricultural development discussed so far in this book have to do with increasing the harvest each year from the land already in farms, and in its present condition. Two additional ways to accelerate development are: (1) to improve the quality of the land already in farms and, (2) to bring additional land into cultivation.

When one sees the extensive terracing of fields and the complicated irrigation systems that farmers have completed in the past and are using today, there can be no doubt that they understand the value of this kind of investment very well. Think, for example, of the millions of acres of rice terraces, some in very mountainous country, built hundreds of years ago and still being farmed.

The question is not *whether* to improve and expand the land base for agriculture. Instead, the important questions are *where* this should be done and *how*. In making these decisions, the relative cost of different kinds of land improvement and the length of time before each can be completed and become productive are important considerations.

For the immediate future, investment to improve good land now being cultivated is the most promising approach. This involves improvements to retain rainfall and to increase the efficiency of irrigation and rain water, the improvement of existing irrigation distribution systems, and provisions for drainage.

For the long-run future, the opening of new land and the tapping of new water resources offer wide opportunities for expanding agricultural production. However, the bringing into cultivation of sizeable areas of new land involves costly investments in roads and other community facilities, services and assistance to settlers, land clearing, and sometimes irrigation systems and drainage as well. These are essential parts of a program to bring new land into cultivation if it is to be successful.

Since heavy investments and long-term financing are required for such projects, along with a great deal of administrative machinery and organizational effort, it is extremely important that they be undertaken only after competent surveys of the soils and water resources, and appraisals of the project's economic and administrative feasibility, have been made. Many large projects have been started prematurely and have become a political burden to the government, a disappointment to the farm settlers, and a serious waste of scarce investment funds which could have brought much higher returns had they been used for increasing the productive capacity of lands already being cultivated.

Improving the Land Already in Farms

Where a farmer depends entirely on rainfall, the productive capacity of his land can often be increased by various types of terracing, land levelling, water run-off controls and drainage facilities. Such land improvements are designed to increase the water-holding capacity of the soil in order to conserve moisture, or to provide for drainage at seasons when there is too much water. There is much present farm land that needs drainage. This can seldom be satisfactorily arranged by one farmer acting alone. In most cases a wider system is required, serving many farmers. Land improvements of this sort often can be made at relatively low cash cost by using local manpower and draft animals at slack seasons of the year.

Similarly, there are many areas with ample opportunities for small-scale irrigation development, where farmers can build their own irrigation systems with only a little outside help by drawing water from shallow wells or by diversion from a stream. Governments of several African countries are encouraging farmers to do this.

Irrigation may extend the agricultural land base or increase production on present farms. With population growth, expansion of land is important for the future, but efforts to improve land already in cultivation should not be neglected in favor of more glamourous new lands programs.

Finally, there are many established irrigation systems where the distribution of water is not that required for increasing productivity at the present time. In some cases, improvements of the canal system, including prevention of seepage, provision for drainage, and better control over canal maintenance and water application can substantially increase the productive capacity of the land. India and Pakistan, for example, have extensive irrigation systems built many years ago and designed not to achieve maximum crop production but to protect against total crop failure in periods of drought. Because of this, the canals and their distributaries were laid out to make it possible to give some water to three to five times as large an area as can be provided with the amount of water needed for high levels of crop production using technologies available today. In some of these areas, it is possible to adjust the area under irrigation to the requirements of an efficient cropping system within the available water supply. In other areas it has become difficult at this stage to correct this situation except by the construction of large numbers of wells to draw on the resources of underground water.

Bringing New Land Into Cultivation

Opening new lands for cultivation is a popular and glamorous type of agricultural development, whether it is a matter of clearing the forest and replacing it with cultivated farms or of extending irrigation in arid regions so that the desert can be cultivated, or of reclaiming lake bottoms or tidal flats from the sea.

The major valid argument in favor of bringing new lands under cultivation is that they extend the physical base for agriculture *in the long-run*. New large irrigation schemes, along with the roads and the many community facilities required, take 5 to 10 years or more for construction, and then another 10 years or so before the new settlers have developed an intensive and well-balanced farming system to make full and efficient use of the new land and water resources. For the immediate years ahead, by far the greatest increase in food and fiber production will have to come from the lands already in cultivation.

Another argument for programs to develop new lands rests upon the fact that it is often easier to introduce new farming systems and techniques, new land tenure arrangements, new sizes of farms, and other changes in new farming areas than in old established ones, because many traditional obstacles are absent in new areas. New types of farming on these lands, new types of extension services and credit and cooperative organization, and new incentives guiding farmers and villagers toward a more modern system of production and local community organization, can provide a demonstration from which the whole country can benefit. At the same time, however, it must be recognized that the cost of such comprehensive projects is very high.

Where the opening of new lands for cultivation requires large-scale irrigation or drainage installations heavy investments are needed. Such schemes should be most carefully prepared on the basis of detailed soils and water surveys, experimental trials of possible cropping systems, and other social and economic studies. Moreover, the financial and administrative feasibility of each project must be competently appraised before it is started. Where there is doubt about the government's capacity not only to finance, but also to plan, organize and administer such complicated and costly schemes right

165

Large scale irrigation or drainage installations require heavy investments and competent planning based on reliable information about the area, its soils, climate, and inhabitants. For the Iranian Khuzestan Development Project, the participation of the World Bank was obtained for financing and FAO has assisted in the provision of soils experts for surveys and training of local technicians.

through to the development of modern farming systems, it would be more advantageous to the country to utilize these investment funds to increase agricultural production on lands already in farms and delay the more complicated schemes until a later date.

In most of the large-scale irrigation schemes of the recent past, much too little attention has been given to the development and organization of efficient distribution and utilization of irrigation water, to the planning and servicing of modern farming systems, marketing facilities, extension and credit agencies, and related research and training activities. Without these follow-up programs, much of the value of the initial large investment is lost.

Even where new lands can be brought under cultivation without large-scale irrigation investments, it is necessary to plan new land settlement projects on the basis of soil, water and crop surveys. Land has to be cleared of timber and brush, and prepared for cultivation. Deep plowing, land leveling, drainage and other costly land improvements are frequently necessary. Although operations like these have become much less expensive in recent years through the use of heavy mechanical equipment, they still require a considerable capital investment. Moreover, schools and medical facilities, community services and agricultural extension are also needed from the beginning, along with the planning of modern farm units, farming methods, and the technical and financial assistance necessary to help the new settler make efficient use of the new land and earn an income distinctly higher than he had before.

There are areas where roads and community facilities are already present, and where settlers can begin to farm new land with relatively little investment and government effort. In parts of Mindanao in the Philippines there are considerable areas with suitable soil and adequate rainfall, where access to highways can be provided without too much expense. Here, the agricultural frontier could move steadily ahead for some time with proper technical guidance and organizational assistance, without massive investment and government effort. Similar opportunities for such relatively inexpensive settlement activities on new land can also be found in some regions of Africa and Latin America. These opportunities deserve more attention, and settlers deserve more encouragement and guidance than they have received in the past. Many small settlement projects of this type can add up to a substantial contribution to the agricultural progress of a country.

In summary, land improvements on existing farms can often be made with small investments and use of local manpower, and can have an immediate effect on production. Bringing large new land areas under cultivation requires costly capital investments, especially if large-scale irrigation systems are involved. Complex and long-term administration is also necessary if the project is to be carried through to completion with new farming systems using modern practices. Such projects usually require 10 to 20 years to bear full fruit.

This is not to say that large schemes to bring new land into cultivation are not often advisable. Most countries need all of the good agricultural land they can bring into cultivation. Mexico has done particularly well in bringing new irrigated lands into cultivation. It is important, however, that long-range projects not divert attention from opportunities to improve the quality of land already being farmed. Its productive capacity can be vastly increased. This needs to be done whether new lands are brought into cultivation or not. The cost is lower, and the return can come much more quickly. Seldom can the land area of a country be doubled, or even increased by fifty percent, through developing new lands, but it is often possible to increase by fifty percent or even to double the yields of crops on the existing land.

CHAPTER 14

National Planning
For Agricultural Development

It should be clear from previous chapters that the policies and actions of governments have a profound effect on the rate of agricultural development. These policies and actions are of many kinds. The policies include those regarding land ownership and tenancy, taxation, foreign exchange, tariffs, domestic prices, and public investment. The actions include programs of education, research, credit, market regulation, land development, construction of transport facilities, and may include others as well.

National planning is the process of deciding what the government is going to do with respect to each of these policies and actions affecting agricultural development within a given period of time. In making these decisions, a government must face up to the question of what is needed, at the moment, to move agriculture forward, and what preparations need to be made now in order to meet needs that can be foreseen in the near future. It must also take into account the amount and nature of its resources of money and manpower that can be applied to meeting the needs of agriculture. These resources are never adequate to do all that might be done, so choices have to be made on the basis of the relative priorities of different policies and programs. Since these priorities keep changing, national planning must be continuous, providing for changes in national policies and programs to keep them pertinent to the changing needs of agriculture.

One of the serious problems involved in effective national planning arises from the fact that proposals with respect to policies and programs arise from many sources. Administrators of present programs usually recommend that their current activities be continued and expanded. Proposals with respect to land policies may come from politicians, professors, or private citizens. Suggestions regarding price policies may come from industrialists, farmers, labor leaders, or bankers. Proposals of various kinds may come from members of planning boards who are assumed to be neutral with respect to the demands of different interested groups of officials or of citizens, but who have the limitation of not being intimately aware of the operating problems within all of the various governmental policies and programs that may be proposed.

It is because of this problem that it is important for many persons, in all of the groups making proposals regarding governmental policies and programs, to have an over-all understanding of what is required to get agriculture moving, in addition to technical competence in their own fields. Only where this condition is met can the best possible reconciliation of conflicting proposals be made and the best national plan result.

What lessons can be drawn from the facts reviewed in this book for the improvement of national planning for agricultural development?

1. The "Essentials" Deserve the Highest Priority

If our analysis in this book is correct, then the highest priority in planning should be given to assuring that all of the essentials are present in the best agricultural regions of the country: markets for farm products, new technology, the local availability of farm supplies and equipment, incentives to farm operators, and transportation facilities.

Talking about accelerating agricultural development is useless unless these essentials are present. In too many cases, countries have undertaken elaborate programs of one or another of the accelerators without having provided for the essentials.

2. The Accelerators Can Help Where the Essentials Are Present

Giving highest priority to the essentials does not mean that work on the accelerators should be postponed until the country has been cov-

170

ered with the essentials. No country is starting from scratch in agricultural development. Small parts, at least, of almost every country may already be reasonably well supplied with the essentials. In those places, local pilot projects of extension education and production credit, aids to group action by farmers and national planning can serve two purposes. They can speed up agricultural development in regions where the essentials are already reasonably adequate, and they can perfect methods of operation that can later be extended to other parts of the country. They can also train personnel to begin staffing later projects in other parts of the country.

Although efforts to increase production on lands already in farms should normally take precedence over efforts to expand the land base, there are circumstances where the initial steps toward land development projects should not be delayed.

The priority of essentials over accelerators, therefore, applies primarily to regions within a country; it is not a *time* priority for national planning as a whole.

3. Only Part of Agricultural Development Can Be Planned

A national plan can cover only what the *government* does about agriculture. In other words, governmental activities and policies can be planned but agricultural production cannot be, except in an indirect fashion and therefore incompletely.

The extent to which the facilities made available by the government are used depends on decisions and actions by many private citizens. *Farmers* make the critical decisions about what crops they grow, the methods they use, the credit they employ, and how much of their produce they market. For greatest productivity these decisions must be left to farmers because of the wide variations in natural conditions both between and within individual farms. Even on state-operated or collective farms, production is affected by how well each worker does his delicate job of tending crops and livestock. And a considerable amount of production in socialist economies takes place on small individually-operated plots.

Much of the marketing of farm products and distribution of farm supplies and equipment is carried out by private merchants even in

171

countries where these functions are partly performed by cooperative societies or by government agencies. Governmental credit never completely replaces private lending.

As a matter of fact, if one looks at the countries where the rate of growth of agricultural productivity is highest, these are invariably the countries that are not trying dogmatically to be either "private enterprise" or "socialist," but countries that recognize that agriculture is, and must be, both private and public. Agriculture develops most rapidly when decisions as to whether a particular function affecting agriculture is to be private or public or a mixture of both are arrived at "pragmatically": how can each particular function be performed most efficiently and effectively, in the light of presently existing circumstances in that particular country.

Furthermore, variations in weather conditions from year to year are certain to affect agricultural production, without any regard for the wisdom of planning or the efficiency with which plans are carried out. Sometimes plans are given credit for increased production really due to favorable weather. At other times plans are blamed for failures for which the real reason is a poor season. Progress in agricultural development, therefore, cannot be judged accurately by looking at the record of production for only one or two years but only by the trend over several years.

The planning of governmental activities affecting agriculture is important but it can never be more than partial.

4. Planning Should Be By Agricultural Regions

Any plan for agricultural development for a country needs to be made up of separate plans for different agricultural regions within the country. The measures to spur agricultural development usually need to vary enormously from one region to another. Some regions are potentially more productive than others, and the needs of the country at a particular time may be such that increasing production of specific crop or livestock products, found in certain regions but not in others, may be considered most important. Two regions may have the same potential but one may be much farther along in the development process than the other. In the region that is more advanced there may be a greater need for such measures as increased

172

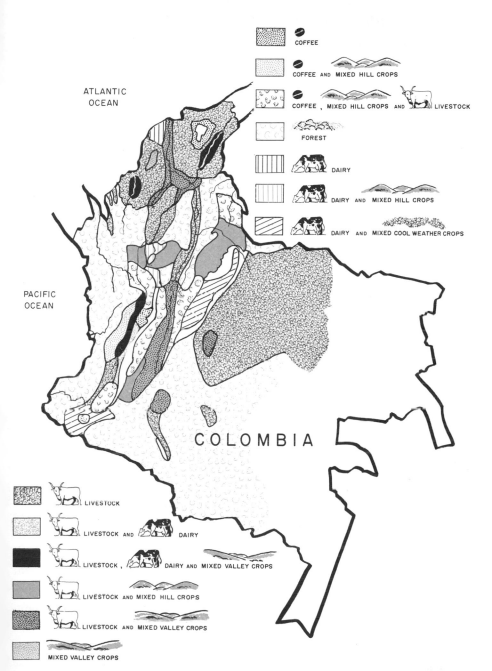

COFFEE

COFFEE AND MIXED HILL CROPS

COFFEE, MIXED HILL CROPS AND LIVESTOCK

FOREST

DAIRY

DAIRY AND MIXED HILL CROPS

DAIRY AND MIXED COOL WEATHER CROPS

ATLANTIC
OCEAN

PACIFIC
OCEAN

COLOMBIA

LIVESTOCK

LIVESTOCK AND DAIRY

LIVESTOCK, DAIRY AND MIXED VALLEY CROPS

LIVESTOCK AND MIXED HILL CROPS

LIVESTOCK AND MIXED VALLEY CROPS

MIXED VALLEY CROPS

Different farming-type areas require different plans for development.
The part of Colombia shown above has types of agriculture dominated
by a tropical crop (coffee), by livestock and by cool season crops.

173

storage facilities for farm products, expanded facilities for production credit and improved provision for market information to farmers. In the other, the greater need may be for improving the transportation network and undertaking a different kind of research in pursuit of new technology.

Concentrating the government's attention on the regions that are already most productive will usually give the greatest quick increases in total production. Meanwhile, people in the poorer regions feel they have as much right to public facilities as anyone else. This conflict can be reduced by developing different kinds of plans for different regions. Some regions, however, are so poor in natural agricultural resources that it is useless to try to develop them, at least before dramatically more productive uses for the land have been developed.

5. Production and Market Possibilities Must Be Considered Jointly

It is not what a region can grow that determines its agricultural potential. It is what it can grow that can be profitably sold. This potential can be changed by improving transport and marketing facilities. Until this is done, however, the development of each region is limited by its markets.

What are these markets for each region? To determine these requires estimates of the probable demand for selected crop and livestock products *and the geographical location of these demands either within the country or abroad.*

Such estimates should include the demand over the next few years for those food products increasingly desired by people as their incomes rise such as milk, fruits, meat and eggs. The demand for such foods rises rapidly with the growth of cities and with rising industrial wages. Moreover, to the extent that these are new types of production in a region it may be easier to increase production of them, partly because they have no "cultural history," no ritual significance attaches to them, there may be fewer taboos, and farmers do not have previous habits or traditions about producing them that they would have to change.

It is not necessary to have demand projections for all crop and livestock products but only for those for which new technology is already available and that give promise of rapid increase if the necessary facilities, information and skills are made available to farm operators.

6. Planning Should Be Directed More at Increasing the Profitability of Farming than at Increasing Production of Specific Farm Commodities

We should keep reminding ourselves that the objective of each farm operator is not to achieve maximum physical production within any one crop or livestock enterprise but the maximum margin of returns over costs for his farm business as a whole. Insofar as he is producing for the market, he does not really care whether he grows rice, or tobacco, or maize or sugar cane. Planners may want to increase the production of rice and may arrange to increase fertilizer availability to make that possible. But if it is more profitable to farmers to use the fertilizer on sugar cane, that is what they will do. If they are correct in their judgment about relative costs and returns they are doing more for agricultural development than if they had done what the planners hoped they would.

Certain farm equipment and supplies can be used on any one of several farm enterprises, and farmers will use each where it will have the greatest effect on net returns. Every farmer knows that what he does about one enterprise affects others in his farm business and he takes account of this.

For these reasons, planners need to learn to view the agriculture of their country as being made up of *thousands or millions of farm businesses of various sizes and types,* rather than as so many acres of each of a number of different crops plus so many head of various kinds of livestock. Planning is productive only as it increases the opportunities for each of these many farm businesses to be more productive, whatever the precise combination of farm enterprises may be on each.

This is not to say that the government cannot influence the amount of selected commodities that farmers produce. It can do this by the policies it adopts affecting prices. It can do it by its allocation of re-

175

search effort to selected crops and livestock. It can do it by having its extension workers put special emphasis on them, but this can be successful only if the price relationships are favorable.

7. Many Investments Require Time to Become Productive

We have noted in Chapter 13 that large schemes to expand land and water resources take many years to become fully effective. The same is true of many other investments for agricultural development. Research stations must be efficiently operated over a period of years before many of their experiments succeed and are tested to the point where farmers can have confidence in the new methods they provide. Extension services have to operate for several years before farmers gain confidence in them, partly because it takes each extension worker several years on the job to become really competent and to deserve the farmer's confidence.

Plans for agricultural development must be far-sighted. They must foresee needs in the future and get started with investments that require a number of years to begin to pay off.

8. The Quality of Each Activity is More Important Than Its Quantity

In their eagerness to spur agricultural development many countries are launching country-wide programs of extension education, production credit and primary and secondary school systems. This is understandable. Such wide-spread activities can be self-defeating, however, if adequate attention is not paid to their quality. Too frequently, the number of workers is considered more important than arrangements for in-service training. In research, laboratory equipment is often given more attention than the selection of top-priority problems for study and administrative arrangements for team research on selected projects by specialists from different fields.

"It is not how much you spend but what you buy with it" is a slogan that ought to be on the wall of every office where planning is done. Wise allocations of public revenues to different activities must include careful review of the plans for each activity and of the way in which it is to be administered.

176

9. Certain Activities Should Be Coordinated Locally

Four activities are so dependent on each other that they should be closely coordinated in each locality. These are:

1. the availability of farm supplies and equipment
2. local testing of these inputs
3. extension education
4. production credit

Purchased supplies and equipment are essential if agricultural productivity is to rise. Local testing helps convince farmers that these inputs can be productive. Extension education helps farmers learn how to use them. Production credit helps enable farmers to buy them.

Where these activities are conducted by separate persons and national agencies, whatever coordination there is among them too frequently is only in the national headquarters. The most important place for this coordination to occur, however, is locally.

If local coordination is accepted as the first requirement, then the central organization of each activity can be geared to this.

10. Important Relationships Related to Agricultural Development Cannot Be Expressed in Numbers

Much of agricultural planning consists of alloting government revenues to different activities. It would be helpful if one could calculate in advance just how much return in increased productivity could be expected from each expenditure of government funds, but this cannot be done.

Recognition that production credit will accelerate the adoption of improved practices by farmers does not mean that it is possible to predict how much faster particular improved practices will be adopted, with respect to which crops, and how much effect these will have on total production or on overall farm earnings. Estimates of current losses due to field rats do little to aid in estimating what value of crops will actually be saved by the expenditure of a given amount on a rat control program. To recognize that a plan should include opportunities for technicians and officials to grow in professional ability does not give a numerical answer to the question of how much this will increase farm productivity in a given period of time. It is

Good data is a requirement for good planning. Information for planning of Peruvian agriculture is being gathered by an agricultural census taker.

fairly safe to assume that elementary and secondary schooling are worth more than they cost, but whether an additional sum spent on them is to be preferred to establishing a research station is a question to which no mathematical equation can give an answer.

This becomes a problem in national planning precisely because mathematical tools *can* give dependable answers to *certain parts* of planning. They should be used for every task for which they are appropriate. But qualitative judgments are the only method possible for putting all parts of the plan together. These must always be based on less-than-perfect information and knowledge, but there is no alternative.

As thorough an understanding of agriculture and of agricultural development as can be achieved is, therefore, the most important qualification for each person involved in the planning process. Too frequently, plans are drawn up by administrators each of whom is really competent only in his own technical field. Each such person owes it to his country to develop a broader viewpoint and competence. In addition, there should be some persons involved whose *primary* commitment and concern is to agricultural development as a whole.

11. Planning Should Take Account of the Desires and Complaints Voiced by Farmers

There is frequently a considerable difference between the judgment of planners and the judgment of farm operators as to what measures are needed for agricultural development at a particular time. Sometimes, and on some points, one group is closer to the truth, sometimes the other. Plans for agricultural development should not be based solely on the desires and the complaints of farm operators, for the horizon of their thinking is usually the boundaries of their own locality. On the other hand, plans for agricultural development are always likely to be more soundly based if they are drawn up in full knowledge of what the judgments of farmers are as to what they need in order to move ahead.

12. Plans for Agriculture and for Industry Should Be Jointly Considered

Agricultural development is affected by the nature of the country's plans for industrialization. What can be done in agriculture depends on what farm supplies and equipment are available, and the prices for these. If domestic manufacture will lower the cost, this will help agriculture. If it involves protective tariffs that raise the cost, this will retard agricultural development unless some type of subsidy of the cost to farmers is also provided.

General industrialization increases the number of non-farm wage earners and thereby increases the domestic market demand for farm products. It also may increase the consumer goods available in rural markets, thereby increasing farmer incentives to produce and sell more in order to buy some of these consumer goods for their families.

179

13. Planning Should Include Critical Assessments of What Is Already Being Done

Too frequently, planning covers only new activities, or financial allocations for older ones without critically reassessing their quality. Frequently more contribution can be made to development by improving the quality of activities already under way than by starting new ones.

Moreover, such assessments of what is now happening should review the agricultural development that has taken place recently in certain parts of the country, trying to discover what has led to this. Such a review may indicate how additional development could be secured in other regions.

14. Planning Should Be Continuous

There is not, and cannot be, any one plan for achieving agricultural productivity. The programs needed to spur agricultural development at any given time are different from region to region and they change constantly within each region.

Public policies affecting agriculture should also be under continuous review. An example here is land reform measures that establish the conditions of tenure under which farmers operate. At one point in time it may be wise for a country to limit the size of agricultural holdings to a chosen maximum in order to break up feudal patterns of land holding and increase the incentives to the individual operators of smaller farms. But a time frequently comes when changes in agricultural technology and increasing off-farm employment opportunities make it wise to modify this policy. No policy should be regarded as permanent, nor should a country refrain from establishing a particular policy when it is needed just because it will have to be changed later.

The key to effective national planning is a *thorough understanding of agriculture and of agricultural development*. Good plans can never be made by compromises among specialists each of whom really understands only his own part of the task. Each specialist who participates in planning needs a general understanding of the whole of agriculture and of agricultural development.

PART

Getting
Agriculture Moving

"Enthusiasm and determination are the engine; skills
and knowledge are the tools; occupations and citizen-
ship are the opportunities."

What does it take, then, to get agriculture moving and to keep it moving in the direction of higher and higher levels of productivity? The answer to which most of this book points is "almost everything." We have seen that when we talk about a progressive agriculture we are not talking just about cultivating land and tending livestock. Instead, we are forced to speak of roads and price relationships and research organizations and trade and governmental policies. We must think of industrialization and the forms it takes, education and its content, banking, laws, and administrative efficiency in governmental departments.

182

Some of these requirements (discussed in Part II) are essential. They are like the five spokes and parts of the rim of a wheel on which agriculture can move. None is useful without the other four.

Markets for farm products provide one:

New farm technology adds a second:

The local availability of farm supplies and equipment is a third:

Adequate incentives for farmers provide the fourth:

Transportation facilities complete the wheel:

Now agriculture can *move*.

But this is a crude wheel. It can be made much more efficient by adding the five accelerators: education for development, production credit, group action by farmers, improving and expanding agricultural land, and planning for agricultural development. Each of these is like a ball bearing or like grease that reduces friction at the axle. Or it is like a tire that lets the wheel roll more easily over stones or other obstacles that may lie in its path. On a wheel equipped with these accelerators agricultural development can move much more rapidly.

183

All of the essentials and the accelerators have their effects by changing the facilities available to farmers and the conditions under which farming is carried on. If the essentials and accelerators are to be effective in advancing agriculture, they must do so by affecting one or more of the *elements of agriculture* discussed in Part I. Ultimately, any measure to encourage agricultural development must:

1. modify the production process of agriculture, or
2. change the behavior of farmers, or
3. change the nature of individual farms, or
4. change the relationship between costs and returns in individual farm businesses.

Many measures for agricultural development affect more than one of these. All of these elements must keep changing if agriculture is to move forward.

When one takes this kind of an over-all view of it, agricultural development appears to be a complex task, and it is. Fortunately, no one of us is asked or expected to work at all of it, or even to keep all of it in mind very much of the time.

Reading a book like this is like stopping one's work for a few minutes to look at the whole task to see how the job is coming along and to be reminded of what needs still to be done. It is like a consultation among members of a hockey or basketball team before or during the game as to the exact methods by which they hope to score. It is like travelers who are hiking across hilly country without roads or paths stopping for a few minutes to decide the route they should follow for the next portion of the journey. Discussing agricultural development with other people, checking one's own ideas against theirs, trying to reach decisions about what is to be done next can be helpful but this doesn't get the job done, either.

To get the job done, in any undertaking as complex as agricultural development, requires breaking it down into smaller parts with different people working at each part of it. It requires *specialization* by each of us, with each of us spending most of his time working on his own special task.

The chapters of this book merely indicate the variety of activities within which many specialized tasks must be performed if agricultural productivity is to move ahead. They review the fact that to achieve agricultural development thousands or millions of people must concentrate on managing farm businesses, cultivating crops and tending livestock. Other thousands must operate marketing facilities that bring farm supplies and equipment to farms and move farm products from farms, protect them, transport them, and make them available where consumers can use them. Hundreds of people must concentrate on continuously finding more and more productive methods of farming either by importation or by development through research. Thousands must be employed in manufacturing farm supplies and equipment, in education for development, and in providing production credit.

Each specialized task has its own requirements of skills and knowledge. Yet all require certain characteristics if they are efficiently to serve the cause of agricultural development.

Work, Learning, Experimentation, Empathy

The first is *work:* hard work, careful work, continuous work, long hours, years and years of work. We take this for granted in the case of farmers but it is equally necessary in all of the specialized tasks related to agricultural development. The research worker must not only plan his experiments but he must carry them through, step by step, doing each task exactly when it needs to be done without regard to official holidays, or weather, or considerations of whether he feels like it at the moment. The extension worker must plan his days carefully, keep moving from one farmer or group of farmers to another, meeting them when it is convenient for them rather than for him, preparing for method and result demonstrations thoroughly and carrying them through effectively. It takes effort for him to do this, day after day, remaining enthusiastic and interested even when he is weary from having done the same thing day after day and month after month.

Agricultural development is work, hard work, for everyone: farmers, production credit agents, merchants, legislators, editors, teachers, planners, administrators and all of the others who are involved in the process.

185

The second requirement in all specialized tasks is *learning*. An agriculture that is developing is always changing. Today's methods need to be different from yesterday's. This means that none of us ever knows all he might, or needs to, about his own task. He must always be learning.

Some of this learning can come from just being thoughtful and observant about what one is doing. Some can come from reading and from visiting and talking with others engaged in similar work. We can learn from each other. And we can keep learning by taking full advantage of any opportunities we have for in-service training.

The third requirement in each specialized task is *experimentation*. The ways we have been taught may be good ways, but are there not better ones? Sometimes we act as though all new methods have to come from someone else, from some "expert." Who are these others? Who are these experts? They must be people engaged in the same specialized tasks we are or they would not have been aware of the problem. They must be someone just like ourselves except that they have experimented. Many more experiments fail than succeed. It is the persistent experimenter who, failing often, sometimes succeeds. Any of us can be an experimenter within his own task; all of us should try.

Finally, most specialized tasks require some *empathy*: the ability to see things from the other person's point of view. Certainly the extension agent has to be able to put himself in the place of the farmer and the administrator needs to be able to imagine how his subordinates feel and what they need from him. The credit agent needs to understand how he would feel if he were a farmer and walked a long distance to secure a loan only to find the office closed when it should be open, or if he were sent from one office to another, and still another, unnecessarily or without understanding exactly why it was necessary. And the research worker, if he really wants the results of his research to spur agricultural development, must understand the problems of extension workers and see that his results are expressed in language that farmers and extension agents without specialized research training can understand.

Each of us, whatever his specialized job, can do it better if he has this quality.

Special Problem Features of Agricultural Development

In addition to the above components of each specialized job—work, learning, experimentation, and empathy—there are several special features of agricultural development for which we must be prepared if we are to get agriculture moving.

High investment costs. Agricultural development does not come free. It has a high cost. It requires substantial *investment:* this investment is the purchase price of an agriculture that will come back over future years in the form of higher agricultural production and incomes. We are accustomed to accepting the necessity of spending millions of dollars to build a steel plant, knowing that this is the price we must pay for being able to produce steel. The same necessity faces us with respect to agriculture, except that the kinds of things in which we must invest are so varied: irrigation wells and channels, fences between crops and livestock, transportation systems, storage and marketing facilities, banking systems, research stations, schools and universities, and many others.

In other words, agricultural development involves high costs borne today to lay the foundation for greater productivity tomorrow. Part of these investments is in "physical capital": irrigation dams, factories, research equipment, farm improvements. Another part of them is in increased human skills, knowledge, inventiveness, and productive capacity.

Social and economic conflict. Another feature of agricultural development is that it cannot be achieved without conflict. Administrators, in general, do not like to change their ways. Many scientists dislike seeing their research results out-dated. Monopoly traders and lenders do not like to see their domains invaded. Landlords are displeased when their land is taken over to be divided among the landless. And many people just don't want change.

There is something of this in all of us. The differences are largely in degree. It is not simply that some of us are conservative and others are progressive. Each of us is some of both, but the proportions differ.

Every change in technology, every change in organization, every change in laws or in official policy changes the economic and political relationships between persons and groups of persons in the society.

This is one of the inescapable costs of progress. Sometimes the situation becomes explosive, and frustration and anger burst out into revolution. Sometimes the conflict is so mild that its results are grudgingly tolerated by those who feel they have been hurt.

In the long run, increasing production provides more for everyone, and most of those initially hurt by necessary changes become better off than they were before. In the meantime, if we believe in trying to achieve higher levels of living and the greater productivity that can make this possible, then we have to be prepared to face the conflicts between the interests of different persons and groups that are affected.

Unbalanced development. With so many requirements for agricultural development, it is practically impossible to keep them all in balance. There are bound to be times when farmers are eager for more fertilizer than is locally available, while in another region stocks of fertilizer may go unsold for lack of sufficient demand. There may be times when extension agents "run out of something to extend" because research has lagged behind, or when a new research development offers new production opportunities that cannot rapidly be seized because the extension service is inefficient or production credit is inadequate. Canal irrigation may be available before farmers know how to use it, or it may extend to so many farms that none gets as much water as it needs.

Unbalanced development is not always the result of poor planning. Sometimes it is, but with the best planning in the world unbalanced development is to be expected. It is a feature of progress. To walk one pushes forward until "out of balance" and then takes a step. *The only balanced agricultural economies are those that are stagnant at a low level of productivity.*

Instead of weeping over such imbalances, we should constantly seek to identify the currently limiting factors—those that are lagging behind—and make special efforts to speed up progress on them without ceasing to make still further progress on key factors that are already reasonably adequate.

A high rate of investment, a constant series of social and economic conflicts (mild or severe) and unbalanced progress on different factors affecting agricultural productivity—these are universal features of agricultural development.

Persons Produce Development

Agriculture gets its energy from the sun but agricultural development gets its drive from persons.

Enthusiasm and determination are the engine. Individual tasks within agricultural development are all performed by persons. The amount of energy they put into these tasks depends on how much enthusiasm they have for their work and how determined they are to do it successfully and well.

The power of enthusiasm and determination is greatly multiplied when a whole people, or a large number of them, become united in a kind of crusade for development.

The Mexican Revolution is usually dated as starting about 1912. Yet fifty years later one could still see signs on walls, and slogans in newspapers: *"For the Revolution!"* When this kind of contagion spreads through a people it becomes virtuous to experiment, to run risks, to invest great effort, and to achieve progress. When this happens the enthusiasm and determination of tens or hundreds of thousands of people become a powerful driving force toward development.

Such a constructive contagion never reaches all members of a society. Some people are always followers or reluctant riders, dragging their feet. But the hard working and progressive innovators and experimenters provide the engine for development through their enthusiasm and determination.

Skills and knowledge are the tools. Enthusiasm and determination are not enough. Farmers must have the skills of cultivation and of farm management, and knowledge of progressive methods of farming, of costs, and returns, and of markets. Research workers must have the skills of scientific thinking and of experimentation and broad knowledge of the technical field in which they work. Administrators must have the skills of organizing people to work together and knowledge of how to accomplish their assigned tasks. The same is true for each specialized task. It is only as a person has skill and knowledge that he can contribute to development, and it is only as his skill and knowledge keep growing from year to year that he can keep

189

up with progress in his society and continue to make a contribution.

Occupations and citizenship are the opportunities. When one surveys the broad requirements for agricultural development it becomes clear that each person has two kinds of opportunity for contributing to development.

One is in his occupation.

The other is through his influence as a member of society. The attitudes of each person are a part of "public opinion." What he believes and expresses publicly makes it easier or harder for himself and others to pursue development actively and openly. He may, in addition, have an influence, large or small, on governmental policies and legislation affecting agriculture. These two—occupation and citizenship—are his opportunities.

What Can I do to Spur Agricultural Development?

The last section of this chapter each reader must write for himself. Almost *every* person in *each* society can do something to raise agricultural productivity. Some can do it only as consumers and as citizens who help to form public opinion. Every farmer, agricultural technician or administrator, legislator, editor, professor, manufacturer, merchant and banker, can do more.

What can *you* do, now, without waiting for conditions to change or for someone else to do something first?

Go back over this book, chapter by chapter. Look at each of the subtitles in each chapter. As you do that, finish this book by writing on this and the following pages the specific things you can do to increase the rate of agricultural development in your country.

I can . . .

I can . . .